BEGINNERS GUIDE
TO BUILDING
ELECTRONIC PROJECTS

ALSO BY THE SAME AUTHOR

BEGINNERS GUIDE
TO BUILDING
ELECTRONIC PROJECTS

by
R. A. PENFOLD

BERNARD BABANI (publishing) LTD
THE GRAMPIANS
SHEPHERDS BUSH ROAD
LONDON W6 7NF
ENGLAND

©1977 BERNARDS (Publishers) LTD

I.S.B.N. 0 900162 68 6

First Published September 1977
Reprinted January 1980
Reprinted May 1981
Reprinted March 1983
Reprinted January 1985

Printed and Bound in Great Britain by Mayhew McCrimmon Printers Ltd

CONTENTS

CHAPTER 1 COMPONENTS

Page

CHAPTER 2 TOOLS

CHAPTER 3 CIRCUIT BOARDS

CHAPTER 4   CASES

Chapter 1

COMPONENTS

Electronics is considered by many people to be a highly technical subject which is only of interest to academics. It undeniably is a highly technical subject, but this need not deter the average individual from taking up electronics as a hobby, since it is quite possible to ignore the technicalities and concentrate on the more practical aspects. It is quite possible to construct various items of electronic equipment without having even a basic understanding of the electronic principles involved.

As one would probably expect, there are disadvantages to completely ignoring the technical side of the subject, the primary one being that if a fault develops in a piece of equipment, or a newly constructed item of gear fails to work, fault finding without any technical knowledge is usually a rather difficult and time consuming business. There is often no visible evidence of a fault.

Even this problem is not insurmountable, because problems with faults will be rare provided good quality components are used and instructions are accurately followed. Also, whether one intends to or not, a certain amount of technical knowledge will inevitably be picked up by the electronics constructor. With experience, some constructors develop a sort of sixth sense for locating faults.

The purpose of this book is to enable the complete beginner to tackle the practical side of electronics, so that he or she can confidently tackle projects such as those featured in the popular magazines and books on electronics. Subjects such as component identification, tools required, soldering, constructional methods, etc. will be covered, and practical examples in the form of simple projects will be given.

Component Identification

One of the first problems the beginner comes up against is that of identifying components, which often have their values marked in some form of code. Even if a component has its value written on in ordinary figures and symbols, confusion can still arise if the units used on the component are not the same as those used in the article or book. For instance, as we shall see later, a 1000pf capacitor and a 0.001mfd. one have precisely the same nominal value.

This section will deal with what the various types of component look like, how their values can be determined, what their circuit symbols are, and so on.

Resistors

Virtually every electronic project uses a number of these, and they are probably used in larger quantities than any other type of component. Physically a resistor usually looks like a small tubular shaped object with a wire protruding from the centre of each end. The value is usually shown by a system of colour coding, with resistors of this type having four coloured bands around their bodies.

Resistor values are in units known as Ohms, but since the Ohm is a rather small unit, resistor values are often specified in kilohms or megohms. One kilohm is equal to 1,000 ohms, and so a value of 2,200 ohms would normally be written as 2.2 kilohms or just 2.2k (k is the accepted abbreviation for kilohm). One megohm equals 1,000,000 ohms, and so a value of say 10,000,000 ohms would more commonly be given as 10 megohms or just 10M.

The abbreviation for the word ohm is the Greek letter omega (Ω). The unit of resistance is named after Ohm, the German electrician.

The circuit symbol for a resistor is shown in Figure 1(a), and Figure 1(b) shows the way in which the coloured bands are arranged around the body of a resistor. The first two bands indicate the first two digits of the value, and the third band is the multiplier. The first two digits are multiplied by the figure represented by the third band, and this gives the value of the component. The four band indicates the tolerance of the component. The following table shows the figures represented by the various colours.

Colour	Number represented if colour appears as the first or second band	Number represented if colour appears as the third band
Gold	Not used here	0.1
Black	0	1
Brown	1	10
Red	2	100
Orange	3	1,000
Yellow	4	10,000
Green	5	100,000
Blue	6	1,000,000
Violet	7	Not used
Grey	8	Notused
White	9	Not used

The fourth band represents a percentage, and the table which is shown below indicates which colours represent which tolerance percentage.

No fourth band	± 20%
Silver	± 10%
Gold	± 5%
Red	± 2%
Brown	± 1%

Thus a resistor having yellow, violet, red and gold coloured bands has a value of 4700 ohms, or 4.7k, and its actual value is within plus or minus 5% of that nominal value. This information is derived in the following manner. As will be seen from the tables above, the yellow band shows that the first digit is a four, and the violet one shows that the second digit is a seven. This gives us 47 which then has to be multi-

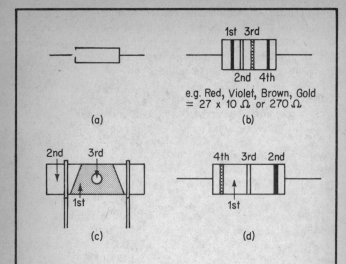

Fig. 1. (a) Resistor circuit symbol, (b) ordinary resistor colour coding, (c) and (d) coding sometimes used for resistors having high power ratings.

plied by the third band, which is red and represents 100. Thus the value of the component is 47 x 100 ohms, or 4700 ohms (4.7k). The fourth band is gold which corresponds to a tolerance of 5%. No resistor has precisely its marked value, and the tolerance marking gives guaranteed maximum limits. In this case the actual value of the component must lie between 4465 ohms and 4935 ohms.

Very occasionally a resistor with a fifth coloured band might be encountered. The first band will be salmon pink in colour, and this merely indicates that the resistor is a high stability type. Also very occasionally a resistor having a silver third band may be encountered, and this indicates a multiplier value of 0.01. Resistors of such low value are only very rarely used however.

It is worth noting that if, for example, 10% resistors are specified for use in a project, it is quite in order to use types having a lower tolerance (e.g. 5% types), since these will obviously be within the specified 10% tolerance. It is not satisfactory to use a higher tolerance component than is specified in the components list.

Resistors are available in what are termed preferred values. The E12 series of values is as follows: 10, 12, 15, 18, 22, 27, 33, 39, 47, 56, 68, 82. Resistors are also available in values which are ten times these values, one hundred times them, and so on up to about 10 megohms. Values above 10 megohms are not readily available to the amateur. Resistors of one tenth of these values are also available, but resistors below one ohm are not readily obtainable.

This system may seem a little unusual to the beginner, but it is really quite logical. If you study the values you will find that each one is about 20% higher than its predecessor. Close tolerance resistors (5% tolerance or less) are often available in what is called the E24 series of values. This consists of all the values in the E12 series plus the following: 1.1, 1.3, 1.6, 2.0, 2.4, 3.0, 3.6, 4.3, 5.1, 6.2, 7.5 and 9.1. Therefore this range increases in increments of about 10%. These additional values are not often used.

Another form of resistor coding is sometimes used, and this consists of a combination of letters and numbers which are marked on the body of the component. There is always a total of four letters/numbers. The first three always consist of two numbers and one letter. The numbers indicate the first two digits of the value, and the letter indicates the units that are being used and the position of the decimal point. The letter R indicates that ohms are the units, K indicates the use of kilohms, and M the use of megohms. This last marking is always a letter, and this indicates the tolerance as follows: F = ± 1%, G = ± 2%, J = ± 5%, K = ± 10%, M = ± 20%.

The following examples should help clarify this system.

    1R0J   = 1 ohm 5%
    10RF   = 10 ohms 1%

K10K	=	100 ohms 10%
1KOJ	=	1k 5%
10KG	=	10k 2%
M10G	=	100k 2%
1MOF	=	1M 1%
10MK	=	10M 10%
10MK	=	10M 10%
5R6K	=	5.6 ohms 10%
56RJ	=	56 ohms 5%
K56J	=	560 ohms 5%
5K6G	=	5.6k 2%
56KM	=	56k 20%
M56K	=	560k 10%
5M6M	=	5.6M 20%

A variation on this system is sometimes used, whereby the units/decimal point indicator cannot come at the beginning of the coding. This necessitates the use of an extra digit for some values. For example, 220 ohms 10% would be 220RK rather than K22K, and 330k 2% would be 330KG rather than M33G.

Apart from a value in ohms, a resistor also has a power rating. This is not marked on the component in any way, and if this rating is unknown it can usually be gauged from this physical size of the component. The larger the resistor the higher is power rating. In most circuits these days the power rating of the resistors used is not important because the widespread use of transistors and integrated circuits rather than valves has resulted in the total power consumption of most circuits being very small. Thus, even if subminiature 1/8th watt resistors are used in the majority of modern circuits there is little chance of one burning out. In fact the opposite is more likely to be the problem, with there being too little space available if, for instance, a ½ watt component is substituted for a ¼ watt one.

High power rating resistors are occasionally used in such projects as power amplifiers and power supplies. These sometimes have a slightly modified form of colour coding as shown in Figure 1(c). No indication of the tolerance is provided with this arrangement. Another variation which is sometimes used on high power resistors is shown in Figure 1(d).

Capacitors

These are used almost as frequently as resistors, and some types are similar in appearance to resistors, but are physically larger than miniature resistors. With the widespread use of printed circuit boards and similar forms of construction, many capacitors are now of the form shown in Figure 2(a). Here both leads come out of the same side of the component so that it readily plugs into a printed circuit board. Ceramic capacitors are often in the form of a disc (and are usually advertised as disc ceramics) as shown in Figure 2(b). They sometimes have a rectangular body, and are then usually called ceramic plate capacitors. Another type of ceramic capacitor is the tubular type (which is actually hollow!) and this has the appearance shown in Figure 2(c).

Silvered mica capacitors always used to have the appearance shown in Figure 2(d) and were comparatively large, but these days they often take the form shown in Figure 2(e), and are comparatively small.

Higher value non-electrolytic capacitors often have the form shown in Figure 2(f).

The resistors and capacitors described so far are non-polarised types, which simply means that it does not matter which way round they are connected into circuit. Non-polarised capacitors of more than about 1 or 2 mfds. in value are expensive to manufacture, and tend to be physically rather large by modern standards. High value capacitors are therefore mainly of the electrolytic type, and these usually take the form shown in Figure 2(g). There is an indentation in one end of the components body, and this indentation is next to the positive (+) leadout wire. Some electrolytic capacitors are intended for printed circuit mounting and take the form

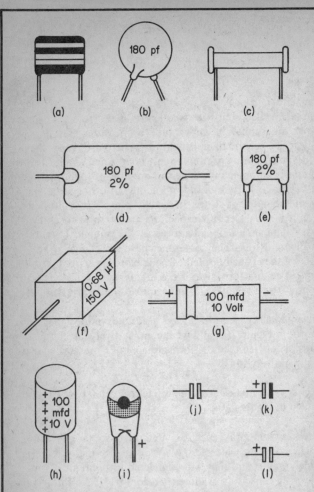

Fig. 2. (a) A radial lead capacitor, (b) a disc ceramic, (c) a tubular ceramic, (d) a silvered mica type, (e) a modern silvered mica type, (f) some high valve non-electrolytic types take this form, (g) an electrolytic, (h) vertical (p.c.b.) type electrolytic, (i) a tantalum bead, (j) capacitor (non-electrolytic) circuit symbol, (k) electrolytic circuit symbol, (l) alternative for (k).

shown in Figure 2(h). The positive and negative leadout wires are then indicated by the appropriate + or − mark on the body of the component.

A special type of electrolytic capacitor known as a tantalum bead is sometimes used in amateur electronic projects, although it is only very rarely that this type of component is specified. They are physically quite small, and are usually only about 10 mm long by 6 mm in diameter. They have the appearance shown in Figure 2(i).

This covers most types of fixed capacitor which are in use at present, with the exceptions of trimmer and variable capacitors, which will be considered separately.

The circuit symbol for a non-electrolytic type capacitor is shown in Figure 2(j), and the symbol for an electrolytic type is shown in Figure 2(k). Sometimes the alternative which appears in Figure 2(l) is used for electronic types.

The values of capacitors are expressed in Farads, and this unit is named after Faraday. The farad is an extremely large unit, and capacitor values are normally expressed in terms of micro farads, nano farads, or pico farads. A micro farad is one millionth of a farad, a nano farad is one thousandth of a micro farad, and a pico farad is equal to one thousandth of a nano farad. The word micro is often abbreviation to the Greek letter mu (μ), and farad is usually abbreviated to the letter f. Thus micro farad is often abbreviation to μf, or sometimes to mfd. Nano is usually abbreviation to the letter n, and pico to the letter p. Therefore capacitor values are often expressed in terms of nf and pf.

Often the value of a capacitor is simply written on, and occasionally the tolerance is also given. Very often the tolerance is omitted, and it is not usually considered to be an important parameter, as it is in the case of resistors. Of greater importance usually is the maximum working voltage, which for some capacitors is as low as three volts. This parameter is usually written on the component along side the capacitance value. 15

Some capacitors have their values and other parameters marked in a form of colour coding of a similar type to that used on resistors. An example of this type of capacitor is the popular Mullard C280 series of components. These have five coloured bands on their bodies, as shown in Figure 3(a).

The top three bands show the value of the capacitor in exactly the same way as the first three bands of a resistor indicate its value. However, whereas the value of a resistor is expressed in ohms, in this case the value is in pico farads. The fourth band indicates the tolerance, and here the colour coding differs somewhat from that used on resistors. The colours used and the tolerances they indicate are as follows: Black = ± 20%, White = ± 10%, Green = ± 5%, Orange = ± 2.5%, Red = ± 2% and Brown = ± 1%. Most of the C280 capacitors that are supplied by retail sources are of either 10 or 20% tolerance. The fifth band indicates the maximum working voltage of the component, and this is either red in the case of a 250V component or yellow for a 400V one.

Thus a C280 capacitor which has coloured bands which are yellow, violet, orange, white, red, (reading from the top downwards of course) has a value of 47 x 1000pf, or 47000pf in other words. This value can also be written as 0.047mfd. or 47nf. Its tolerance is 10% and it has a working voltage of 250V.

A similar system is used for some disc ceramic capacitors and most tubular ceramic types, which have coloured dots rather than bands to indicate the value and tolerance. This is shown in Figure 3(b) (disc ceramics) and Figure 3(c) (tubular ceramics). The working voltage is not indicated on this type of capacitor. Occasionally a tubular type with five dots may be encountered. If the first dot is ignored, the remaining four indicate the value and tolerance in the usual way. The first dot indicates the temperature coefficient, and is of no significance as far as the beginner is concerned.

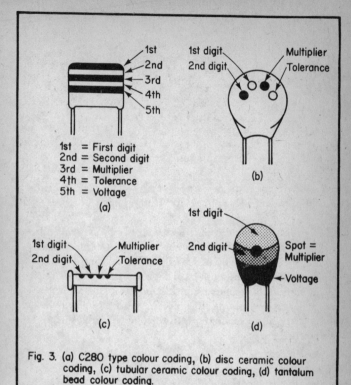

Fig. 3. (a) C280 type colour coding, (b) disc ceramic colour coding, (c) tubular ceramic colour coding, (d) tantalum bead colour coding.

The tantalum bead capacitors which are available to the amateur almost invariably use the form of colour coding shown in Figure 3(d). The colour coding for the first two digits is the same as for resistors and other capacitors, but the colour coding for the multiplier is different. The multiplier colours and their corresponding values are as follows:

Colour	Multiplier	Working Voltage
Grey	0.01	25V
White	0.1	3V
Black	1	10V
Brown	10	Not used here
Red	100	Not used here
Yellow	Not used here	6.3V
Green	Not used here	16V
Blue	Not used here	20V
Pink	Not used here	35V

The above table also shows how the lowest coloured band indicates the working voltage of the component.

Thus a tantalum bead capacitor which has brown, green, and white coloured bands (reading from top to bottom), and a white spot, has a value of 15 x 0.1mfd., or 1.5mfd. in other words. Note that tantalum bead capacitors are all high value types, and that the value is in mfds and not pfs. The white dot indicates a working voltage of 3V. This spot also indicates the polarity of the leadouts, with the one to its right being the positive (+) one.

Diodes
These are the most simple devices in the semiconductor family. They have the appearance shown in Figure 4(a), and the circuit schematic shown in Figure 4(b). Almost without exception, the coloured band around one end of the diode indicates that the leadout wire it is nearest to is the positive (+) one. Unfortunately there are just a few diodes where this band indicates the negative (−) lead. Such components are very rare though.

Most electronic components are fairly tough and do not need to be handled with any great care. There are a few exceptions however. For example, capacitors which use the same form of construction as the C280 types, or any similar form, can be damaged if the leadout wires are pulled out sideways from the

body of the component. This can result in a leadout wire
being parted from the body of the component. If it is necessary to bend a leadout sideways from the body of this type of
component it is better to simply bend it round ones fingernail.

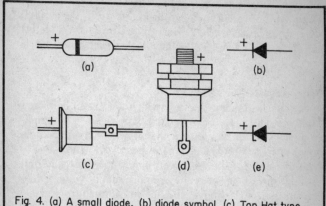

Fig. 4. (a) A small diode, (b) diode symbol, (c) Top Hat type
rectifier, (d) Stud type rectifier, (e) Zener circuit symbol.

A similar problem can arise with diodes, which usually have
glass encapsulations. Holding the body of the component
and then bending a leadout wire close to where it enters the
body of the diode can result in the glass casing fracturing.
Again it is possible (and advisable) to bend the leadout wire
around the end of one's fingernail without putting any
significant pressure on the body of the component.

There is a form of diode which is called a Rectifier, and this
is really just a diode which has been designed to handle higher
power levels than an ordinary diode. Most of these look very
much like an ordinary diode, except the case is usually made
of plastic and can be quite large. Also the leadout wires are
usually much thicker. Some rectifiers have a metal case and
have the appearance shown in Figure 4(c). Devices which are
designed to handle very high currents usually have the form of
construction shown in Figure 4(d). A considerable amount of
heat can be generated in this type of rectifier, and it is designed so that it can be bolted to a piece of metal. This piece of

19

metal is known as a heatsink, and it enables the rectifier to dissipate the heat it generates.

There is a special kind of diode which is called a zener, and this is used as a simple form of voltage stabiliser. It has the circuit symbol which is shown in Figure 4(e). Physically a zener diode looks much the same as an ordinary diode or rectifier which is designed to handle a similar power level.

Transistors

Bipolar transistors are the type which are most commonly employed, and these come in two basic types, n.p.n. and p.n.p. The circuit symbols for these types of component are shown in Figures 5(a) and 5(b) respectively. These two types of transistor are really very much the same, the only real difference being that they require supply voltages of opposite polarities (n.p.n. circuits are normally negative earth whereas p.n.p. ones are usually positive earth).

Other types of transistor in common use are the Junction Gate field effect transistor (Jugfet), the Metal Oxide Semiconductor field effect transistor (MOSFET), the Dual Gate Metal Oxide Semiconductor field effect transistor (d.g. MOSFET), and the Unijunction transistor (U.J.T.). The circuit symbols for these devices are shown in Figures 5(c), 5(d), 5(e), and 5(f) respectively.

Transistors are housed in a variety of metal and plastic encapsulations and have either three or four leadout wires. When an ordinary bipolar transistor has four leadouts, the extra one simply connects to its metal case and is called a shield connection. The circuit diagram for a bipolar transistor (n.p.n.) which has a shield connection is shown in Figure 5(g).

The terminals of a bipolar transistor are called the base, emitter, and collector. The equivalent terminals of a field

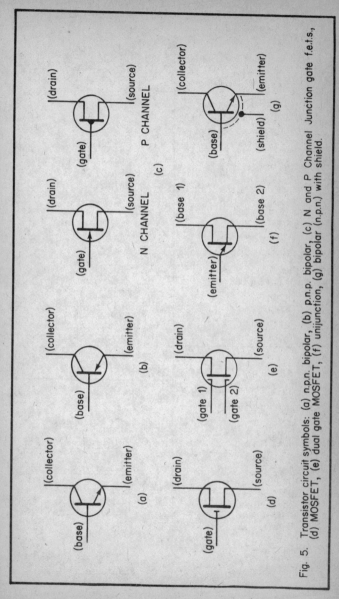

Fig. 5. Transistor circuit symbols: (a) n.p.n. bipolar, (b) p.n.p. bipolar, (c) N and P Channel Junction gate f.e.t.s., (d) MOSFET, (e) dual gate MOSFET, (f) unijunction, (g) bipolar (n.p.n.) with shield.

TO-18 (or larger TO5) Case
Metal case
often connects to collector.

emitter
base
collector

N.P.N.	P.N.P.
BC107	BC177
BC108	BC178
BC109	BC179
BFX84	BC186
BFY50	BC187
BFY51	BFX29
BFY52	BFX88
2N706	BCY71
2N2369	BCY72
2N2369A	2N2904
BSY95A	2N2905
2N2219	
2N1711	

TO-72 Case

c   shield
e   b

N.P.N.	P.N.P.
BF115	AF124
BF167	AF125
BF173	AF126
BF184	AF127
BF185	

c   shield
b   e

N.P.N.	P.N.P.
BF180	AF139
BF181	AF178
BF182	AF179
BF183	AF180
BF200	AF181

TO3 or similar Case
Case is collector connection

b

e

2N3055	BDX18
BDY20	OC26
BD121	OC35
BD123	AD149
AD161	AD162

collector

e
c
b

BD131	BD132
BD135	BD136
BD137	BD138

Fig. 6.

22

TO-1 Case

N.P.N.
AC176
AC187

P.N.P.
AC128
AC188

TO-92a Case

BC182L	BC212L
BC183L	BC213L
BC184L	BC214L
2N3704	2N3702
2N3707	2N3703
2N3708	
2N3709	
2N3710	

2N2646
(Unijunction)

Lockfit Type

P.N.P	N.P.N
BC147	BC157
BC148	BC158
BC149	BC159
BCX31	BCX35

3N140
3N141
40673
40841

N.P.N.
BF194
BF195
BF196
BF197

BF244
2N3819
(Jugfets)

(Jugfets)

2N5457
2N5458
2N5459
MPF102
MPF103
MPF105

effect type are gate, source, and drain, respectively. A dual gate type, as the name suggests, has two gate terminals which are simply called gate 1 (g1) and gate 2 (g2). The unijunction transistor is a rather unusual device which is not used in the same way as the other types at all. Its terminals are called the emitter, base 1, and base 2.

Details of the leadout configurations of the relevant transistors are usually provided in constructional articles, but if a piece of equipment is being constructed from a circuit diagram such information may not be provided. The information provided in Figure 6 should prove helpful, and this gives details of the leadout configuration of many popular types of transistor. Note that this diagram shows base views of the components (i.e. the transistors are viewed looking onto the leadout wires).

Thyristors and Triacs
These devices are used in D.C. and A.C. control circuits respectively and the smaller types, which are most frequently used in circuits for the amateur, are identical in appearance to a TO5 encapsulated transistor. Like transistors, they both have three leadout wires.

Thyristors are sometimes called by the alternative name of silicon controlled rectifier, or S.C.R. for short. They have the circuit symbol shown in Figure 7(a). The three terminals are called the anode, cathode, and gate. The terminals of a triac are called anode 1, anode 2, and gate. It has the circuit symbol shown in Figure 7(b).

The diagram which appears in Figure 7(c) shows connection details for some common types of thyristors and triacs. Note that these devices are often advertised by their maximum current and voltage ratings rather by a type number.

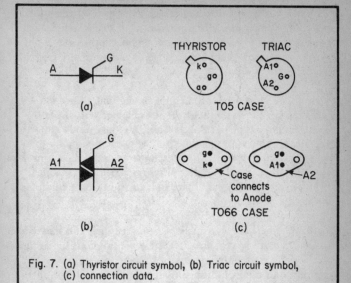

Fig. 7. (a) Thyristor circuit symbol, (b) Triac circuit symbol,
(c) connection data.

Potentiometers

This is a form of variable resistor, and it has the appearance
shown in Figure 8(a), and the circuit schematic which appears
in Figure 8(b). Electrically there are two basic types of
potentiometer, the logarithmic (log.) type and the linear
(lin.) type. Log. potentiometers are used for applications
such as volume controls and A.F. gain controls, whereas
linear types are used for most other purposes.

Most of the potentiometers which are used these days are of
the carbon type (i.e. their resistive track is made of carbon),
but Wirewound types are occasionally used. These have a
track which is made of resistance wire which is wound around
a ring like former which is usually made from a ceramic
material. These are usually only used where it is necessary
for the component to be able to handle a fair amount of
power. They are also used in some precision applications
where their greater accuracy is beneficial. They are generally

25

somewhat larger than carbon types, and are only generally available as linear types. Carbon types are available in values from about 1k to 2.2M, but wirewound potentiometers tend to have come in a rather lower range of value (usually from a few ohms to no more than 100k).

It should perhaps be mentioned in passing that a third electrical category of potentiometer is available, and this is the antilogarithmic type (antilog.). These are only used in a few specialised applications and are only very rarely used by the amateur. Another type of potentiometer is the dual gang type, and these merely consist of two potentiometers joined together (one behind the other) and controlled by a common spindle.

Potentiometers are also available as preset types, and these are frequently employed in circuits. They are not controls of the type which are mounted on the front panel of equipment and operated via a control knob, but are usually mounted on the circuit board along with the other components such as resistors, capacitors, and transistors. They are available in various shapes and sizes and some are properly encased like

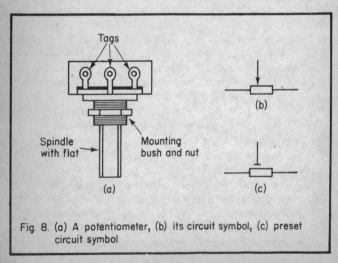

Fig. 8. (a) A potentiometer, (b) its circuit symbol, (c) preset circuit symbol

ordinary potentiometers, but mostly they are of open construction (known as skeleton prests). Electrically they are only available as linear types, but physically there are two types. Those for vertical mounting and those for horizontal mounting. They are adjusted by means of a screwdriver. They have the circuit symbol which appears in Figure 8(c).

Variable Capacitors
This name is really self explanatory. These are only available in low values with the normal maximum being 500pf. They vary considerably in physical size and appearance, but they all consist basically of two sets of metal plates, one of which is fixed with the other being rotatable by means of a control shaft. By rotating this shaft the two sets of plates can be made to mesh together by any required degree, but they do not come into physical or electrical contact with one another. Often the two sets of plates are only separated by air, and these are known as air spaced capacitors. These have to be constructed to a high degree of precision and are therefore rather expensive and a little delicate, although if handled properly they never seem to wear out. The reason they have to be handled with care is that the set of moving plates is not usually encased in any way, and these can therefore easily be bent or otherwise damaged if the component is carelessly handled. This can cause the two sets of plates to short together.

Usually this type of variable capacitor is supplied wrapped in tissue paper and in a cardboard box. It is advisable to store them in this packing. Never do any drilling, cutting, or similar work to a case or chassis while it is fitted with an air spaced variable capacitor. Always remove the capacitor first. Apart from the possibility of damaging the component, there is also the possibility of swarf getting in between the plates.

Some variable capacitors use a thin layer of plastic or a similar material to insulate the two sets of plates from one another. This insulation layer is known as the dielectric, and capacitors of this kind are called solid dielectric types. They are normally physically smaller than air spaced types and slightly less expensive, but they are not usually suitable for critical applications such as for use in S.W. receivers.

Fig. 9. (a) Variable capacitor circuit symbol, (b) Trimmer capacitor circuit symbol.

Variable capacitors have the circuit symbol shown in Figure 9(a). Like potentiometers, they are available as dual gang types. In fact three and four gang types are not uncommon.

Also like potentiometers, they are available as preset types. These are sometimes called trimmer capacitors or just simply trimmers. They are available in a wide variety of shapes and sizes, and can be either airspaced or solid dielectric in construction. In common with preset resistors, they are adjusted by means of a screwdriver. Trimmer capacitors have the circuit symbol which is shown in Figure 9(b).

Switches

This is another example of a type of component which varies considerably in physical appearance, and there are several general types available. These are slider, rotary, push button, toggle, lever, and key switches. Most people will be familiar with these terms which are largely self explanatory. One exception is perhaps the toggle type. This kind of switch is operated by means of a small metal or plastic lever which is called a dolly.

Electrically the most simple form of switch is the single throw single pole type (S.P.S.T.), and the circuit schematic for this is illustrated in Figure 10(a). This is just a simple on/off switch which is shown in the off position in the diagram. When two S.P.S.T. switches are contained in a single mechanism so that they operate simultaneously they are collectively termed a double pole single throw switch, and they have the circuit symbol which is shown in Figure 10(b).

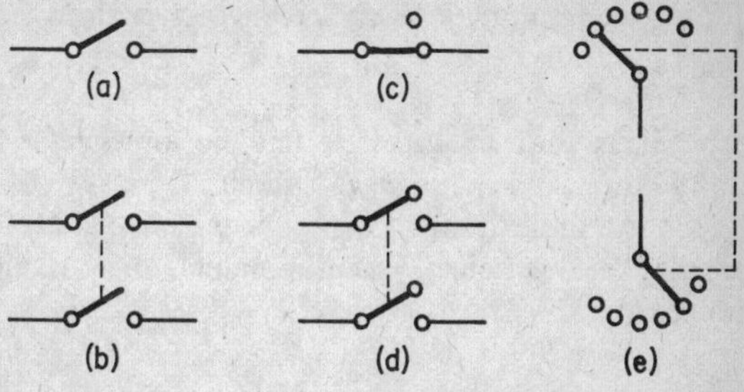

Fig. 10. Switch circuit symbols: (a) S.P.S.T., (b) D.P.S.T., (c) S.P.D.T., (d) D.P.D.T., (e) 6 pole 2 way rotary.

The circuit symbol for a double throw single pole switch is shown in Figure 10(c). Here one contact of the switch can be connected to one of two other contacts. There is a double pole version of this switch which is, as one would expect, called a double pole double throw switch. Its circuit symbol appears in Figure 10(d).

Switches having these four types of contact can come in any of the six types of construction mentioned at the beginning of this section. More complicated types of switch are only generally available in rotary form, and these are sometimes called wafer switches. They are normally described as having 'x' number of ways and 'y' number of poles. Thus the switch for which the circuit symbol is shown in Figure 10(e) would be described as a 6 way 2 pole switch. Many of the rotary switches which are now available have an adjustable end stop so that they can be used in applications where the full number of ways are not required. For instance, many 6 way 2 pole rotary switches can be used for 2, 3, 4, 5 or 6 way operation by giving the adjustable end stop the appropriate adjustment.

D.P.S.T. switches are sometimes ganged with potentiometer so that they can be used in such applications as combined volume and on/off switches. If the switch is used to control the mains then it is normal to use both poles, but when this type of component is used in battery operated equipment it is usual to simply ignore one pole of the switch. The circuit symbol for a potentiometer/D.P.S.T. switch is shown in Figure 10(f).

The dotted lines are used to show that the three items are ganged and controlled by a single spindle. This system is always used to indicate that components are ganged, whether they are switches, potentiometers, or variable capacitors.

Miscellaneous

The components which have been covered so far are the ones in most frequent use, and they have therefore been dealt with in some detail. Now the less frequently used components will be covered in adequate but less complete detail.

Speakers, etc.

Loudspeakers have the circuit symbol which is common in Figure 11(a). Their electrical parameter of importance is their impedance which is expressed in ohms. Commonly available impedances are 3, 8, 15, 16, 25, 35, 40, 50, 75 and 80 ohms, but other less common impedances are available. The main physical parameter is the units diameter in the case of a round or square type, and its length and breadth in the case of an eliptical type.

Loudspeakers must be stored and handled very carefully because they have a diaphragm which is usually made from a paper like material and it is all too easy to accidentally knock a hole in this. Other parts are also easily damaged.

Most people will be familiar with earpieces since these are commonly supplied with transistor receivers and portable cassette recorders. Two main types are available, and these are the low impedance (8 ohm) magnetic type and the high impedance (usually about 100–200k) crystal type. These both have the circuit schematic which appears in Figure 11(b). It is worth noting that although the two types may look very similar they are electrically very different, and although many people believe them to be interchangeable, in many applications they are not.

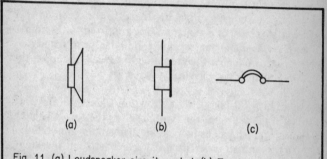

Fig. 11. (a) Loudspeaker circuit symbol, (b) Earphone circuit symbol, (c) Headphone circuit symbol.

High impedance (around 200 to 2000 ohms impedance) magnetic earpieces are available but they are not often used. All types should be handled carefully since the earpiece has a tendency to part company with its lead, and it is often impossible to repair such damage. If dropped they can also easily sustain internal or external damage.

Most people will also be familiar with headphones, and these are also available in both magnetic and crystal types. Crystal headphones are rather rare however. Magnetic types are available with impedances from 4 to 400 ohms, and in both stereo and mono types. It is advisable to treat the less expensive types with some respect as many of these are easily damaged in the same way as earpieces. Headphones have the circuit symbol which appears in Figure 11(c).

Relays

These are an electromagnetic switch and they have several important parameters which are as follows: Coil resistance, maximum and minimum coil operating voltages, number and type of contacts, voltage and current ratings for contacts. It is not usually necessary to use the exact type of relay employed by the author of a book or article, and results should be satisfactory provided the following criteria are met: The coil will operate at the appropriate nominal voltage, the coil does not have a resistance significantly less than the specified type, sufficient contacts of adequate rating are fitted to the component. It does not matter if extra contacts are fitted and their ratings are higher than required, provided of course, that the component is not physically too large.

The symbol for a relay coil is shown in Figure 12(a). The number in the centre of the symbol shows the coil resistance in ohms. The relay coils in a circuit diagram are annotated RLA, RLB, and so on. The number beneath this marking shows the number of contacts associated with that relay coil. The relay contacts are annotated RLA1, RLA2, etc. for the first relay, RLB1, RLB2, etc. for any subsequent relay, and so on.

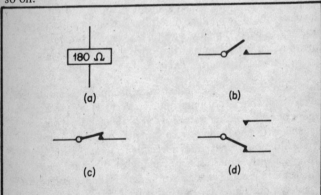

Fig. 12. (a) Relay coil symbol, (b) Normally open relay contact symbol, (c) Normally closed relay contact symbol, (d) Change over relay contact.

Figure 12(b) shows the circuit symbol for a normally close contact. By normally closed it is meant that the contact is closed until the relay coil is energised, whereupon the contact opens. Figure 12(c) shows the circuit symbol for a normally open contact, and Figure 12(d) that for a change over contact.

Batteries
This is another example of a component which should be familiar to all readers. A single cell has the circuit symbol which is shown in Figure 13(a), and a multi-cell type has the one which appears in Figure 13(b). The latter usually has the nominal battery voltage shown next to the symbol.

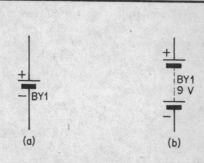

Fig. 13. (a) Circuit symbol for a single cell. (b) Circuit symbol for a multiple cell battery.

Lamps
A signal lamp has the circuit schematic of Figure 14(a) while an illuminating lamp has the one shown in Figure 14(b). A special type of semiconductor diode which is known as a light emitting diode (L.E.D.) is becoming increasingly popular, and this has the circuit symbol of Figure 14(c). This type of lamp has the advantages of extremely low power consumption and long working life. It should be noted that unlike an ordinary bulb, a L.E.D. will only light up if the supply is connected with the correct polarity.

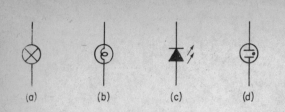

Fig. 14. Circuit symbols for (a) signal lamp, (b) illuminating
lamp, (c) Light emitting diode, (d) Neon.

Neon bulbs are popular for use as mains indicators, and these
have the circuit symbol which appears in Figure 14(d). Neons
which are intended for use as mains indicators have a suitable
series current limiting resistor built in. Neons which do not
have this integral resistor must not be connected direct across
the mains.

Microphones

These have the circuit symbol shown in Figure 15. Like ear-
pieces, they are available in both crystal and magnetic types.
The latter are sometimes referred to as dynamic microphones.
Common impedances for magnetic types are 200 and 600
ohms, or 50k for types which have an integral transformer.
Dual impedance types are available.

In many projects a loudspeaker is used as a sort of magnetic
microphone (intercoms, etc.).

Fig. 15. Microphone circuit schematic.

Coils, etc.

The basic circuit schematic for a coil is shown in Figure 16(a). If it has a ferrite or dust iron core the symbol is modified as shown in Figure 16(b). If the coil has a tapping (a connection made to other than one or other end of the winding), this is indicated as shown in Figure 16(c).

Coils often have more than one winding, and they are then called transformers. Single coils are usually called chokes. Transformers for use in R.F. (radio frequency) and I.F. (intermediate frequency stages) have the circuit schematic of Figure 16(d). Transformers for use in low frequency applications such as audio frequency amplifiers and mains operated power supplies have the circuit symbol shown in Figure 16(e).

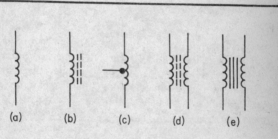

(a)   (b)   (c)   (d)   (e)

Fig. 16. (a) Schematic for a coil, (b) symbol for a coil with a ferrite core, (c) Topped coil schematic, (d) R.F. Transformer circuit symbol. (e) L.F. Transformer schematic.

Photocells

Photoresistors are the most commonly used type of photocell, and these have the circuit symbol shown in Figure 17(a). Phototransistors and photo-darlington transistors are also fairly common, and they have the symbols which are illustrated in Figures 17(b) and (c) respectively.

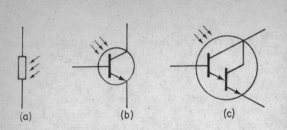

Fig. 17. Circuit schematics for (a) A photoresistor,
(b) Phototransistor, (c) Photodarlington transistor.

Meters

Two basic types of meter are available, the moving coil type
and the moving iron variety. The latter are not often used
since they require a comparatively large operating power,
and they do not have a linear scale. Moving coil meters do
not suffer from either of these drawbacks.

Fig. 18. Meter circuit symbol (ammeter in this case).

The circuit symbol for a meter is shown in Figure 18. The
centre of the symbol is usually marked with the sensitivity
of the meter which is either the current in amps or the voltage
required to produce full scale deflection of the meter's needle.
In the case of an ammeter the sensitivity is likely to be
expressed in milliamps (mA, one thousandth of an amp)
or microamps (μA, one millionth of an amp) as the amp is
rather a large unit.

Integrated Circuits (I.C.s)

These are very important devices which are now used extensively in amateur electronics. They are semiconductor devices which may contain the equivalent of hundreds or even thousands of components. They do not contain individual components though, and the circuit is formed on a small chip of silicon. In this way highly complex circuits can be contained in a very small space indeed. In fact most of the size of an I.C. is accounted for by its encapsulation and leadout wires or pins.

I.C.s come in a wide variety of packages, and some of the popular ones are shown in Figure 19(a). Note that the diagrams show the I.C.s viewed from above, and not from below as was the case for transistors.

With a few exceptions, I.C.s are represented in circuit diagrams in the way illustrated in Figure 19(b). Occasionally, where an I.C. has a very simple internal circuit, this circuitry is shown inside the box.

Some types of I.C. have specific circuit symbols, and a couple of examples are shown in Figures 19(c) and 19(d). These are for an operational amplifier and Norton amplifier respectively. Other types of I.C. amplifier are usually represented by a triangular outline rather than a rectangle, as in Figure 19(e).

Some logic circuits (I.C.s used in computers and similar applications) also have specific circuit symbols, but most of these are unlikely to be employed in projects which fall within the scope of the beginner. The exceptions to this are the gate circuits, which can be used in many simple applications. The circuit symbols for the four common types of gate (OR, AND, NOR, and NAND) are shown in Figure 19(f). This diagram shows the schematic for two input devices, but gates can have any number of inputs.

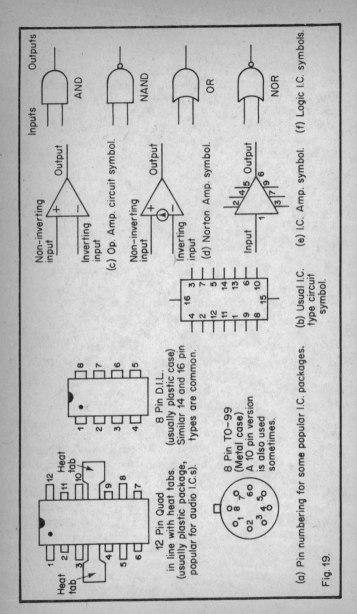

Inputs   Outputs

AND

NAND

OR

NOR

(f) Logic I.C. symbols.

Non-inverting input +   Output
Inverting input —

(c) Op. Amp. circuit symbol.

Non-inverting input +   Output
Inverting input —

(d) Norton Amp. symbol.

Input   Output

(e) I.C. Amp. symbol.

(b) Usual I.C. type circuit symbol.

8 Pin D.I.L.
(usually plastic case)
Similar 14 and 16 pin
types are common.

12 Pin Quad
in line with heat tabs.
(usually plastic package,
popular for audio I.C.s).

Heat tab

8 Pin TO-99
(Metal case)
A 10 pin version
is also used
sometimes.

(a) Pin numbering for some popular I.C. packages.

Fig. 19.

Other Symbols

So far components such as resistors and capacitors have been covered, and so have more mundane items such as batteries, as well as less common devices such as photocells, and lastly and perhaps most importantly the integrated circuit.

This still leaves a few circuit symbols which have not yet been covered, and details of most of these are shown in Figure 20.

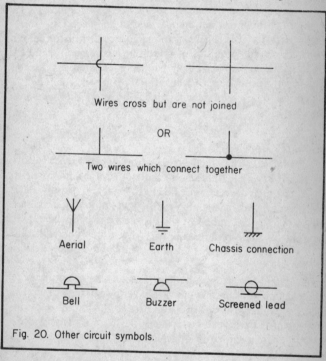

Fig. 20. Other circuit symbols.

It should perhaps be pointed out that circuit symbols may not always be exactly as shown here, but any differences will only be minor ones. For instance, a S.P.S.T. push button switch may well be depicted as shown in Figure 21, rather than as shown in Figure 10(a). Such differences are usually self explanatory.

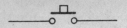

Fig. 21. Circuit symbols may differ slightly from the ones shown here. For instance, a S.P.S.T. push button switch could be represented in the manner shown here.

It is not suggested that readers should try to commit to memory all the information provided so far, since this is not really necessary. It is helpful to memorise the resistor colour code, the circuit symbols of important components, and so on, but this will automatically happen as experience is gained. The main purpose of this chapter is to provide all such information in one place where it can be referred to whenever necessary.

Buying Components

This is an area which seems to cause many beginners a lot of problems. Probably in most areas there is a local components shop, but such sources are unlikely to be able to supply all ones components needs. In fact they will probably only be able to satisfy about half of them, unless one happens to live near one of the very large suppliers. Even then you will still not be able to obtain all the components you require locally.

The reason for this is really very simple. As should have become apparent by now, there is a very vast range of components available at present. Apart from the purely electronic items which have been covered so far, there is also a vast variety of items of hardware which are needed when building any practical project. This includes such things as cases, circuit boards, screws, etc. There are also highly specialised items such as readout displays and ultrasonic transducers. No one supplier is able to supply such a complete range of goods.

It will almost certainly be necessary to obtain many components by mail order, and advertisements of mail order companies can be found in any of the popular electronics magazines. Most of these firms advertise lists or catalogues, and it is advisable to obtain as many of these as possible. One reason for doing so is that you are then unlikely to find that you cannot track down a particular component for a project. Another is that prices for many items seem to vary considerably from one retailer to another, and considerable savings can be made by shopping around.

The reason for such discrepancies in prices is usually quite simple. Retailers tend to specialise in particular kinds of component, although they normally stock a much wider range of components. Bulk buying of their speciality enables them to sell them to the consumer at very attractive prices which ensures rapid sales. This in turn justifies the initial investment in the bulk buy. Thus it is possible to purchase resistors from a firm who specialise in resistors and other passive components, for about a penny each, while some other firms may charge three or four times as much for resistors.

Another reason is that some firms deal mainly in various forms of surplus components, which are usually quite inexpensive.

Although obtaining numerous lists and catalogues may be rather time consuming and expensive in the short term, it is almost certain to prove worthwhile in the long term.

While it must be admitted that in many circuits the exact resistor values, transistor type numbers, etc. used are not too critical, it is advisable for the beginner to avoid the use of substitute and near equivalent components. Using say, a 470k or 680k resistor where a 560k one is specified in a components list will more often than not be quite satisfactory, but not in every case. The problem for the beginner is that he or she is not in a position to know when a substitute or so called equivalent will prove satisfactory.

If a particular component is temporarily unobtainable and you happen to have something similar to hand, then it is probably worthwhile trying it out to see if it is a satisfactory substitute. If the equipment fails to operate for no other apparent reason, then the correct component must be obtained and tried. Nothing has been lost by trying a substitute which was to hand. It is a different matter if a substitute is specially purchased and then proves unsatisfactory.

Chapter 2

TOOLS

Obtaining and identifying components is only half the problem facing the beginner before he or she is ready to actually start constructing equipment. The other basic necessity is the availability of the correct tools, and the ability to use them of course. Many of the tools which are required are quite ordinary ones that probably most households will have already and a description of their use would be superfluous. However, there are a few tools which will probably have to be bought specially, and with which the average person will be unfamiliar. Perhaps the most obvious example is the soldering iron, which is the most frequently used tool in electronic construction.

The purpose of this chapter is to detail the tools required, indicating their relative importance, and the way in which they are used where this is necessary. With the preliminaries then completed, subsequent chapters will go on to describe various constructional methods with some practical examples being provided.

Soldering

It is essential to have a soldering iron from the outset. Probably the best type for general use is one having a power rating of 15 to 25 watts with a bit diameter of about 2.5 mm. Some irons have a range of interchangeable bits of various diameters available, and this is quite a useful feature. In practice though, an iron fitted with a small diameter bit will be found to be satisfactory for just about all applications. There are few occasions these days where a powerful iron having a large diameter bit is needed. All normal electrical soldering jobs can be tackled using a miniature iron. The same is not true of a large iron which is totally unsuitable for fine work, and with modern constructional methods this now includes the majority of soldering jobs.

Instant heat soldering guns are not often recommended for constructional work since they tend to be a little on the large and heavy side. They are generally intended for intermittent use such as in servicing establishments. The type of iron which has to be heated on a gas stove is not really suitable either.

There are many types of solder available, and the type which is used in normal constructional work is a 60% tin — 40% lead type which has a flux core. This is usually available in two thicknesses, 18 s.w.g. and 22 s.w.g. The author always uses 22 s.w.g. solder, although on larger joints 18 s.w.g. solder is a little easier to use. The 18 s.w.g. size is difficult to use on fine work since there is a tendency for too much solder to be applied to the joint. This can result in accidental short circuits.

The purpose of the flux in the solder is to remove any oxide or other coating from the items which are being joined. However, there is a limit to the amount of dirt that the flux can handle, and if you apply solder and a heated soldering iron bit to a badly contaminated lead you will almost certainly find that the solder will not flow onto the lead. It will instead form a globule on the lead. This can be overcome by scraping such leads with a knife so as to remove the dirt, prior to applying solder to a lead. It should then be found that the solder flows over the lead providing a fairly even coating of solder.

This process of covering the ends of leadout wires (or tags, etc.) with solder is known as tinning. When point to point wiring is being used (i.e. leads and tags are soldered directly to one another) it is advisable to tin all tags and leads before attempting to complete any joints. When using printed circuit board construction, or similar constructional forms (all of which are dealt with later on), tinning is less important and is not usually necessary unless a lead or tag is badly contaminated. The leadout wires of modern components are usually designed so that they do not easily oxidize, and so that they can therefore be easily used in modern forms of construction.

Making a Joint

The method of producing a soldered joint is different for point to point construction and for p.c.b. construction and similar methods. We will first consider the point to point method.

As mentioned earlier, the first step is to tin the ends of component leads and tags prior to making a joint. In order to do this one simply places the end of the solder above the end of the component lead (or tag) and then gently place the irons bit onto the solder and then down onto the lead as the solder melts. Apply more solder to the lead if necessary. If oxidation is preventing the solder from taking to the lead this will be immediately obvious.

When the two surfaces which are to be joined have both been tinned, they are placed together and the solder and soldering iron bit are then applied to them in much the same way as was used for the tinning process. Provided adequate solder is used, this should then produce a good strong soldered joint.

In practice this may be rather hard to achieve using this method because one usually ends up holding the soldering iron in the right hand (unless you are left-handed of course) with the left hand having the job of both holding the solder and holding the two components together. This can easily result in some movement of the leads while they are being soldered, and this can in turn lead to a poor soldered joint. It is usually quite apparent when this has happened since the solder on the joint tends to have a rather uneven and dull surface, rather than the usual smooth shiny finish.

The author has found a slightly different approach to be entirely satisfactory. First the two leads are heavily tinned with solder, and then some solder is applied to the end of the soldering iron bit. The two leads are then immediately placed together and the bit is applied to them. In this way a good strong joint is usually produced.

Whatever method is used, always make sure that plenty of solder is used on each joint when carrying out point to point wiring.

P.C.B. Soldering

Basically a printed circuit board consists of a thin sheet of an insulation material such as S.R.B.P. or fibreglass, and on one side of this board there are areas of copper. In the areas where this copper backing is present, small diameter holes are drilled through both the board and the copper backing. The components are mounted on the non-coppered side of the board with their leads passing through the holes. The leads are cut to length on the other side of the board so that about 1 to 2 mm of leadout is left protruding through the panel. The leads are then soldered to the copper backing. The purpose of the copper backing is, of course, to connect the components together in the appropriate manner.

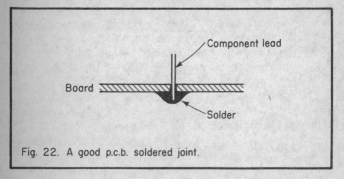

Fig. 22. A good p.c.b. soldered joint.

A side view of a good p.c.b. soldered joint should look something like the diagram which is shown in Figure 22. Here the solder has flowed tightly around the lead and over a fairly large area of copper backing. Apart from providing a good electrical connection, this also provides a firm physical mounting for the component, which is just as important.

Soldering components to a p.c.b. is not quite as simple as one might think. The first steps of fitting the component onto the board and then cutting the leads to length are quite straight forward, but when it comes to making the joint there is the problem that three hands are really required. That is one to hold the soldering iron, one to the hold the solder, and another to hold the p.c.b. and the component in position.

The author gets around this problem in the following fashion. About 100 to 150 mm of solder is unwound from the reel of solder and straightened. The reel of solder is placed on the edge of the workbench so that the unwound solder hangs out over the edge of the bench. One hand is then free to hold the component and the p.c.b. in position beneath the solder while the other hand is free to wield the soldering iron.

Of course, there are other perfectly valid approaches, and if the reader is able to devise one which better suits himself or herself, then this is certainly the one to use.

There are three main causes of problems which are likely to be encountered when soldering components to p.c.b.s, and these are detailed below.

1.   A dry joint. This can be caused by dirt on either the leadout wire or the copper backing. The cleaning of component leads was dealt with earlier. A local patch of corrosion on a p.c.b. can be treated in the same way, but extensive oxidization will require the whole copper backing to be cleaned with either a scouring pad or scouring powder.

A cutaway side view of a dry joint is illustrated in Figure 23. It is usually quite obvious when this occurs because the lead is not anchored to the p.c.b.

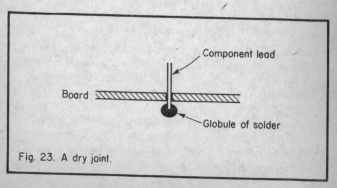

Fig. 23. A dry joint.

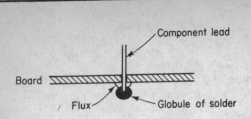

Fig. 24. A dry joint can provide a mechanical bond.

2. A dry joint which provides a mechanical bond. A side view of this type of joint is shown in Figure 24. Here it is flux rather than solder which is securing the lead to the copper track. There is no electrical contact since flux is an insulator. This type of dry joint is obviously rather harder to detect than the type described in 1 above. It can be spotted however, because the solder does not flow outwards over a comparatively large area of copper backing, as in Figure 22. Provided the joint is as shown in Figure 22, then all should be well.

3. Excess solder. This can result in the iron leaving a small trail of solder as the bit is removed, which can in turn result in unintentional short circuits. Very often these are clearly visible, but sometimes the trail of excess solder is so small that it is very difficult to detect visually. You must try to learn the amount of solder that is required to produce a strong joint, and then be careful to use no more than this.

As was the case with point to point wiring, movement of the component can result in a poor joint, particularly if it occurs while the solder is cooling. This is not a common problem when soldering components to p.c.b.s though.

It is a good idea to obtain some soldering experience before undertaking an electronics project. Start by soldering any odd pieces of wire together. Obtain a piece of stripboard and some resistors (because they are the cheapest components available) and try soldering these to the board. Most people soon get the hang of soldering if they experiment a little in this way.

Incidentally, do not be put off if a certain amount of smoke is produced by a newly purchased soldering iron soon after it has been plugged in. This usually happens and it is merely caused by dust and other dirt which has found its way onto the element being burnt off. A certain amount of smoke is usually produced when soldering is applied to the iron, and this is simply due to the flux in the solder burning away.

Heatshunt

One final point about soldering is that virtually all electronic components can be damaged by excessive heat, and so soldered joints must be completed fairly quickly. It should not be necessary to keep the bit on the leadout for much more than about one second.

A few components are very easily damaged by excessive heat, germanium diodes and transistors being the main ones (silicon diodes and transistors are much more hardy). When soldering these it is usual to use a heatshunt between the body of the component and the point which is being soldered. The point of the heatshunt is to absorb the heat which flows up the lead from the joint, and so prevent damage to the component. Commercially produced heatshunts are available, but with a little ingenuity it is possible to devise a home made one. Even a pair of pliers used to grip the lead can be very effective.

Although perhaps not strictly speaking a tool, a soldering iron stand a some sort will be needed. Most manufacturers produce matching stands for their soldering irons. Alternatively some kind of home made stand can be used, but it must be well conceived so that it is likely to prevent rather than cause accidents.

Other Essentials

There are several other tools apart from soldering equipment which should really be regarded as essential. One example is a small electricians screwdriver, and over a period of time it is advisable to obtain an assortment of these in various sizes. The screwdriver which is most frequently used by the author has a blade which is about 3 mm in breadth and about 45 mm long, and so one of around this size should be a good first buy.

A hacksaw and a pair of pliers are also necessities, but presumably these will already be present in most households.

A drill and an assortment of bits are also required. While metric sizes have not completely taken over at the time of writing, they have virtually done so, and so we will only consider metric sizes here. Most potentiometers, switches, and other controls require a 10 mm diameter mounting hole, and so a H.S.S. drill bit of this diameter is essential. M3 and M4 metric screws are frequently used for such things as mounting circuit boards, fastening pieces of a case together, and similar applications. They require mounting holes of 3.2 mm and about 4.3 mm respectively.

These are the drill sizes which the author uses most frequently, but other sizes are used and as you progress in the hobby you will find it necessary to obtain other sizes. Sets of drill bits are available, and it would probably be worthwhile buying one of these, provided they are of a fairly high quality. Alternatively, drill bits of 2.7, 6 and 8 mm, in addition to the three mentioned above, will cover most eventualities. A very small drill bit is required if one intends to make ones own printed circuit boards, and this is covered later on, together with details of the other tools and materials that are required.

Holes which have a diameter of more than about 10 mm are not usually drilled, but are normally made using a device known as a chassis cutter. Details of how to use a chassis cutter will not be provided here since they are supplied with clear operating instructions. Most toggle switches and certain types of socket require a 13 mm dia. mounting hole, and it will be found very useful to have a chassis punch of this size available. If you are interested in audio gear, a 16 mm diameter punch will be useful as DIN sockets require a mounting hole of this size. Those interested in S.W. radio will probably need to obtain a 19 mm diameter punch because a popular range of coils are designed to fit into a

B9A valveholder, which in turn requires a 19 mm diameter mounting hole.

A few components such as speakers and meters require quite large cutouts to be made in the case of the equipment to which they are fitted. A set of miniature files is a useful buy, and a miniature round file can be used to make such cutouts. Miniature files can also be useful if it is necessary to slightly enlarge a hole (because one does not have a drill of precisely the required diameter, for instance). They are also invaluable when it is necessary to produce a small rectangular hole, such as when a slider type switch is to be mounted.

An easier way of making large cutouts in wooden or aluminium panels is to use an ordinary fretsaw. Another alternative is to drill a series of closely spaced holes just inside the periphery of the required cutout. The diameter of the holes is not too important, but they should not be too large, say no more than about 4.3 mm dia. When all the holes have been completed, it should be possible to break out the material inside the ring of holes, and thus produce a rather rough cutout. The edges of this can then be filed out to produce a neat finish.

Although it is possible to cut wires and strip off plastic sleeving without using a proper pair of wire strippers and cutters, it is strongly recommended that the proper tool is obtained. It is possible to cut wire with an old pair of scissors, but in many practical situations this is not really feasible for the simple reason that it is often necessary to cut wires in rather inaccessible places. Proper wire cutters are designed to cope with such situations, whereas scissors are not.

Scissors can also be used to strip sleeving from wire, as can a sharp penknife as well, but with these methods there is a tendency for the outer surface of the wire to be cut. This usually leads to the wire breaking at this point before too long. Again, the proper tool has been designed to cope with this problem.

Finally, a soft lead pencil or a scriber is required for making the positions of drilling points, etc. on cases and chassis.

Useful Tools

There are numerous tools which will be found very useful in electronic project construction, although it is probably possible to get by quite well without them. A list of tools which, in the author's opinion, fall into this category, is given below.

Centre punch	Tenon Saw.
Small hammer.	Vice.
Modelling knife.	Mallet.
Bradawl.	Trimming tools.
Set square.	Scissors.
Large half rounded file.	Hand saw.

Phillips and Posidrive screwdrivers.
Stripboard cutter and pin insertion tool.

It should perhaps be pointed out that many experienced constructors would probably disagree with some items on this list, and would argue that certain items are missing. The reason for this is that each constructor has his or her own way of working and while, for instance, such things as the tenon saw and mallet would be considered important by someone who constructs the cases for his projects, they would probably be considered as virtually useless by the constructor who always uses ready made cases. Trimming tools are essential if you are going to be doing much radio construction, but are of no use if you are not.

Because of this it is advisable to read through the section on essential tools and make sure you have the necessary items right from the outset. Then only obtain the other tools if and when they are needed.

A useful item to have around is a good general purpose adhesive such as a quick set epoxy one. A reel of P.V.C. insulation tape can also prove to be very useful.

Chapter 3

CIRCUIT BOARDS

These days the majority of the components used in electronic projects are mounted on some form of circuit board. There are various forms of circuit board, but they are all basically similar. They consist of a sheet of insulation material which has small holes drilled in it through which the component leadout wires pass. The leadouts are then connected up in some way on the reverse side of the board. There are three types of circuit board which are in common use in amateur electronics; the plain matrix board, strip-board, and etched printed circuit boards.

In this chapter these three forms of construction will be considered, and a practical example of each (in the form of a simple project) will be provided.

Plain Matrix Board
This merely consists of a sheet of insulation material (resin bonded paper) which has been drilled with a matrix of small holes. These boards are available in various sizes, and in two pitches; 0.1 in. (2.54 mm) and 0.15 in. (3.81 mm). The 0.15 in. matrix type seems to be the most popular type for general use, but where I.C.s are used it is more common for the smaller matrix to be used. The reason for this is that the most popular I.C.s have pins that are spaced on a 0.1 in. matrix, and so they are compatible with 0.1 in. board, but will not fit onto the 0.15 in. type.

Plain matrix board is often referred to as plain Veroboard, which is the trade name of Vero Electronics Ltd. However, it is produced by other manufacturers. The way in which it is used is very simple, and merely consists of the components being mounted on one side of the board with their leadout wires being bent flat against the underside of the panel. The leads are then soldered together in the manner required to produce the correct circuit.

Simple Radio

The first project that most newcomers to electronics wish to construct is a simple radio set, and so as a practical example of plain matrix board construction a simple M.W. receiver will be described. Incidentally, the field of radio is the main area in which this type of board is used.

The circuit diagram of the receiver is shown in Figure 25. This is based on the very popular ZN414 radio I.C. and it requires very few discrete components (i.e. components outside the I.C.). Since this book is concerned with electronic construction rather circuit theory, only a brief circuit description will be provided.

There are three main functions which the I.C. performs. Firstly it amplifies the signal which is fed to its input terminal (pin 2) from the ferrite rod aerial, and then it detects this radio frequency (R.F.) signal to produce an audio frequency one. The third function is that of automatic volume control, or A.V.C. as it is often termed. The purpose of the A.V.C. circuitry is to reduce the gain of the I.C. on strong signals so that a fairly constant audio output level is produced, even though the strengths of received signals may vary considerably. It also makes station fading far less noticeable.

VC1 is the tuning capacitor and C1 is a D.C. blocking capacitor. R1 is the bias resistor for the I.C., and the bias current also flows through L1. R2 is the load resistor for the I.C., and the audio output signal is developed across this component. C2 is an R.F. filter capacitor, while C3 couples the audio signal to the output socket and provides D.C. blocking.

The receiver circuit needs a supply voltage of about 1.3 V, and so a simple regulator circuit in the form of D1, D2, C4, and R3 is included so that it can be powered from an ordinary PP3 9-volt battery. S1 is the on/off switch.

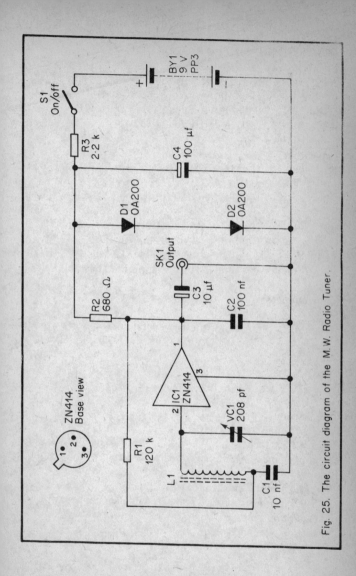

Fig. 25. The circuit diagram of the M.W. Radio Tuner.

55

COMPONETS – SIMPLE RADIO

Resistors

All are miniature $\frac{1}{8}$, $\frac{1}{4}$, $\frac{1}{3}$ or $\frac{1}{2}$ watt 5% tolerance types.

R1   120k (brown, red, yellow, gold)
R2   680 ohms (blue, grey, brown, gold)
R3   2.2k (red, red, red, gold)

Capacitors

C1   10nf type C280 (brown, black, orange, black, red)
C2   100nf type C280 (brown, black, yellow, black, red)
C3   10mfd. 10 v.w. electrolytic
C4   100mfd. 10 v.w. electrolytic
VC1   208pf air spaced variable (Jackson type 01, or any similar type of approximately this value)

Semiconductors

I.C.1   ZN414
D1 and D2   OA200 or similar general purpose *silicon* diodes (BA100, OA202, 1N914, 1N916, 1SJ50, etc.)

Switch

S1   S.P.S.T. toggle type

Miscellaneous

Plain 0.15 in matrix board
3.5 mm Jack socket
High impedance headphones or earpiece fitted with 3.5 mm Jack plug
PP3 battery and connector to suit
115 x 9.5 mm ferrite rod, 32 s.w.g. enamelled copper wire, and insulation tape.
Connecting wire and solder.

The output of the unit will drive a high impedance magnetic earpiece or a crystal type. It will also drive a pair of high impedance headphones satisfactorily, but it is not suitable for use with a speaker or any other low impedance load. An add-on amplifier which can be used to provide speaker reception in conjunction with this unit will be described later.

Board Layout

We now come to the problem of transferring the theoretical schematic diagram of Figure 25 to a practical layout for a plain matrix board. Almost invariably the components are mounted on the matrix panel using very much the same layout as that used in the circuit diagram. This should be readily apparent if you compare the circuit board layout of Figure 26 with the circuit diagram of Figure 25.

There are a few minor differences between the two general layouts, and as an example of this, it will be seen that R2 is drawn vertically in Figure 25, but it mounts horizontally on the circuit board. The advantage of mounting it horizontally on the circuit board is merely that it produces a more compact layout, in that the layout does not then need to sprawl so far up the panel. Similarly, R3 is mounted vertically on the component panel, whereas it is drawn horizontally in the circuit diagram. This reduces the width of the board that is required to accommodate the components, and provides a more compact layout.

Therefore, you can either keep the practical layout as much like the circuit layout as possible, or you can make a few simple modifications which provide a more compact layout without any cramping of components. It is not a good idea to radically depart from the circuit layout when designing a board layout. If you look at the underside view of the board in Figure 26 you will see that none of the wires cross one another. This avoids the necessity to insulate any of them with P.V.C. sleeving. This is usually the case if the physical layout is kept much the same as the theoretical one, but is not likely to be the case if the physical layout is nothing like the circuit one.

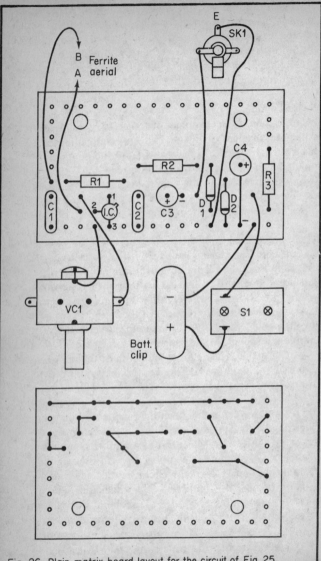

Fig. 26. Plain matrix board layout for the circuit of Fig. 25.

The normal way of mounting a circuit board is to bolt it to the case of the equipment, and for small panels it is usually sufficient to use two mounting points. Three rows of otherwise unused holes are left to provide space for these holes.

Board Construction

It is not difficult to construct a component assembly of this type, and the first step is to cut out a panel of the correct size (9 x 16 holes). It is easier to cut along a row of holes rather than between rows, and either a junior hacksaw or a full size type can be used. In the case of the latter it is advisable to use a blade which is fine toothed, as otherwise the saw tends to cut rather jerkily, and this can result the board fracturing around the cut. The cut edge of the board is almost certain to be a little on the rough side, and it is a good idea to file it to a smooth, neat looking finish.

Then any mounting holes can be drilled, and in this case they can be made using a 3.2 mm drill bit so that they will accept M3 mounting bolts.

Next the components are mounted on the panel, their leadouts are bent over at right angles on the underside of the board, and then they are wired together in the correct manner. There are several ways of going about this, and the one the author usually employs is to first mount the components which connect to the negative supply rail (or positive supply rail in the case of positive earth equipment), and then wire up this rail. Then one by one the other components are mounted and soldered into circuit.

Another method is to start off by mounting all the components, and then cut their leadout wires to length and solder them together as necessary. This method is quite quick and easy where a small panel is to be wired up, but is a little impractical for a very large one. You could start by mounting and connecting any two components which should connect to one another, and then gradually build up the circuit from this point until the panel is complete.

It is not a good idea to simply mount and connect components at random places on the panel, since this is likely to result in wiring errors, especially in the form of missing connections. It is better to work methodically, paying close attention to electrolytic capacitor polarities, etc.

Incidentally, it should perhaps be pointed out that although it was stated earlier that I.C. leadout diagrams show the component viewed from above, whereas transistor leadout diagrams show the component viewed from below, there are a few exceptions to this, and the ZN414 is one of them. This is a rather unusual I.C. in that it is contained in a standard TO18 transistor type encapsulation, and it only has three leadout wires. For this reason its leadout diagram is usually shown as a base view (as in Figure 26), and the same is usually true for other I.C.s which have the same type of encapsulation.

Sometimes when wiring up this type of board you will find that the component leads themselves are not quite long enough to complete the wiring. In these instances it will be necessary to use link wires made from about 22 s.w.g. tinned copper wire to bridge any gaps in the wiring. When soldering the leads together it is not usually necessary to pre-tin them. They are simply cut to length, bent into position so that they are side by side, and then the solder and soldering iron bit are applied to them. Provided an adequate amount of solder is used, a very strong joint should result. Remember that the underside view of Figure 26 is only a diagram, and in practice the wiring will not look as neat as that. This is not too important anyway, concentrate more on producing strong joints and avoiding mistakes.

It will be seen from Figure 26 that a couple of components (C3 and C4) are mounted vertically, and are end on to the panel rather than with their bodies flat against it. This is done merely because this way these components fit better into the physical layout. This method is often used on miniaturised equipment as it provides a more compact layout. In the components list, C280 type capacitors are specified for use in the C1 and C2 positions. Although electrically virtually any 10 and 100 nf components could be used in these positions, physically most other types will not fit in anything like as well. A few types would be too large to fit onto the board at all. This is something to be wary of when ordering components for projects.

Figure 26 shows the way in which this type of panel is most often illustrated, but sometimes the alternative system shown in Figure 27 is used. Here only a component side view of the board is provided, and the underside wiring is represented by the broken lines.

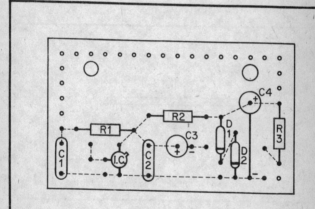

Fig. 27. An alternative method of drawing the board of Fig. 26.

Other Wiring

Of course, not all the components are mounted on the panel, and things like the battery, tuning capacitor, and on/off switch are mounted elsewhere. Where and how they are mounted will be covered in a later chapter which will deal with cases and allied topics. Here we will consider the way in which they are wired up.

The wiring associated with the components which are separate from the panel is illustrated in Figure 26. There is usually a certain amount of interwiring between these components, but this is an exception. This point to point wiring was covered in the section on soldering.

The wiring between the external components and the panel are made using ordinary P.V.C. covered connecting wire, and it is better to use the multistrand type than the single core variety. These leads can be connected to the board in the same way as component leadouts, or via pins. There are two types of pin (in this context), the double sided type and the single sided type. When using plain matrix board it is usually the double sided type which is used, and the manner in which they are used is shown in Figure 28.

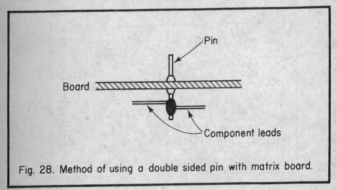

Fig. 28. Method of using a double sided pin with matrix board.

It is advisable to tightly coil the lead on the underside of the panel around the pin before soldering the two together. Then if this solder melts when the connection to the top of the pin is made, the joint will not come apart, and a good joint will be left when the iron has been removed because the solder will then solidify once again. The advantage of using pins is that they enable the board to be completed and mounted in the case before it is wired up to the external components. This is not usually otherwise possible, because the underside of the board is normally obstructed by the case once it has been mounted.

A special tool for inserting pins is available, but the author has always found it to be an easy matter to push them into position using a pair of pliers. The pins are held in place by friction.

It is a good idea to heavily tin pins prior to making a connection to one.

Ferrite Aerial

It is not often these days that it is necessary for the constructor to make a component for a project, but it is sometimes necessary. A fairly common example is the ferrite aerial for a simple M.W. receiver, and this is the case here.

The basis of the ferrite rod aerial is, as one would expect, a length of ferrite rod. This is available in various lengths and diameters, and for the aerial described here a piece 115 mm long and 9.5 mm in diameter is required. If the rod is a little longer or shorter than the specified length this will not matter too much, but it must be of the correct diameter (it may be advertised as 3/8 in. diameter rather than 9.5 mm).

Ferrite is an extremely hard and rather brittle material, and this makes it rather difficult to cut down a longer piece of rod to the required length. If you try to cut it with an ordinary hacksaw for example, you will barely mark the surface of the rod before the hacksaw blade is blunted.

It is possible to cut ferrite rod however, although it is more a matter of breaking than cutting it. The procedure is to cut a groove around the entire circumference of the rod at the point where it is to be broken. This groove should be as deep as possible and can be made using the edge of a half round or triangular file. The rod can then be broken over the edge of a workbench at this point.

This may not produce a very clean break, but any roughness at the end of the rod is totally unimportant from the point of view of performance. As mentioned earlier, ferrite rod is a rather brittle material, and so care must be taken not to break it in the wrong place by accident. It should be handled with care, since if dropped it is not unusual for it to shatter into several pieces.

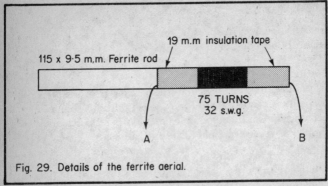

115 x 9·5 m.m. Ferrite rod

19 m.m insulation tape

75 TURNS
32 s.w.g.

A

B

Fig. 29. Details of the ferrite aerial.

Details of the ferrite aerial are shown in Figure 29. The winding starts 19 mm from one end of the rod, and a band of insulation tape is used to hold the end of the coil in place. The winding consists of 75 turns of 32 s.w.g. enamelled copper wire which is wound in a single layer with all the turns going in the same direction. Do not leave any space between turns. Another band of insulation tape is used to hold the second end of the winding in place.

Leadouts wires about 100 mm long are left on the aerial with any excess wire being cut off. The ends of the leadouts then have the insulation stripped off and are tinned with solder before being connected to the component panel. It is not possible to strip insulation from enamelled copper wire using most types of wire stripper, but the insulation is easily scraped off using a pen knife or modelling knife.

The set is quite straight forward to use: the earpiece plugs into SK1, S1 is an ordinary on/off switch, and VC1 is a conventional tuning control. Remember that a ferrite aerial is directional, and to produce the strongest signal it should be pointed at a right angle to the transmitter. Although the set is extremely simple, it should be possible to receive several stations during the day, and many more after dark.

Variation

There is another method of construction which is virtually identical to the plain matrix board type, the only difference being that the constructor obtains an undrilled piece of S.R.B.P. (or similar) and makes the holes in it himself. Of course, there is no need to drill a matrix of holes, they need only be drilled where components are actually going to be mounted. Usually a full size drawing of the panel will be provided, and the constructor traces the drilling points onto the board and then drills them out using a very fine drill bit (about 3/64 in. or 1.2 mm in diameter). The method of construction is then the same as for a plain matrix board.

This method, although once very popular, seems to have become virtually obsolete now, and is only very rarely used. It is much quicker and easier simply to use a plain matrix board.

Stripboard

On one side this type of board is indistinguishable from plain matrix board, but if it is turned over it will be seen to have copper strips runing down the rows of holes, as shown in Figure 30. The idea here is very simple, and merely consists of the components being mounted on the board in the normal way, but with the difference that the leadout wires are soldered to the copper strips rather than direct to one another. The connections between the component are then made via the copper strips.

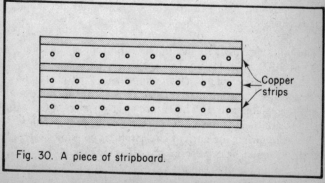

Fig. 30. A piece of stripboard.

Simple Amplifier

As a practical example of a project which is constructed on Veroboard (a trade name under which stripboard is often sold), a simple three transistor amplifier will be described. Such an amplifier can be very useful to have around the electronics workshop, since it is often necessary to employ an amplifier when testing equipment. The amplifier can also be used in conjunction with the simple radio which was described above in order to provide it with sufficient output to drive a loudspeaker.

The circuit diagram of the amplifier is shown in Figure 31, and again, only a brief circuit description will be provided. Basically the circuit consists of two stages, the driver stage which uses Tr1 as a common emitter amplifier, and a complementary emitter follower output stage which utilizes Tr2 and Tr3.

VR1 is the volume control and C1 provides D.C. blocking at the input. R1 is a base stopper resistor and the purpose of this component is to reduce the high frequency response of the amplifier slightly. This gives improved stability, especially when the unit is used in conjunction with a radio tuner. R2 is the bias resistor for Tr1, and R3 plus R4 form its collector load. The purpose of using a split collector load with R4 connected between the bases of Tr2 and Tr3 is to minimise cross-over distortion by providing a small quiescent current through the output transistors. C2 provides D.C. blocking at the output and C3 is a supply decoupling capacitor. S1 is the ordinary on/off switch.

The unit can provide a maximum output power of about 250 to 300 mW into any speaker having an impedance in the range 8 to 25 ohms. Higher impedance speakers can be used, but the maximum output power will then be somewhat less than stated above. The output stage operates in Class B, and basically what this means is that the higher the volume level, the higher the current the amplifier consumes. This provides good battery economy. The quiescent current consumption is only about 6 mA, but this rises to about 50 mA at high volume levels.

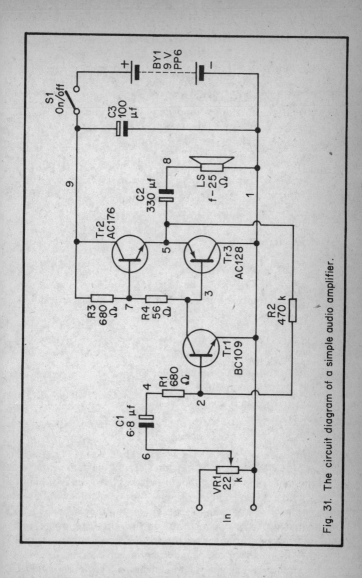

Fig. 31. The circuit diagram of a simple audio amplifier.

67

COMPONENTS – SIMPLE AMPLIFIER

Resistors

All are miniature $\frac{1}{8}$, $\frac{1}{4}$, $\frac{1}{3}$ or $\frac{1}{2}$ watt 5% types.

R1	680 ohms (blue, grey, brown, gold)
R2	470k (yellow, violet, yellow, gold)
R3	680 ohms (blue, grey, brown, gold)
R4	56 ohms (green, blue, black, gold)
VR1	22k log. carbon potentiometer

Capacitors

C1	6.8mfd. 10 v.w. electrolytic.
C2	330mfd. 10 v.w. electrolytic.
C3	100mfd. 10 v.w. electrolytic.

Semiconductors

Tr1	BC109
Tr2	AC176
Tr3	AC128

(Suitable alternatives for the Tr1 and Tr2 positions are AC141 and AC142, or AC187 and AC188.)

Miscellaneous

S.P.S.T. toggle switch (S1)
0.15 in. stripboard (Veroboard)
PP/ battery and connectors to suit
Speaker having an impedance in the range 8 to 25 ohms.
Wire, solder, etc.

Layout

It is not quite as easy to transform a circuit diagram into a component layout on stripboard as it was in the case of plain matrix board. On a circuit diagram the connecting wires can run both horizontally and vertically, and so they can also on a plain matrix board. On a stripboard the copper strips are, in effect, the connecting wires, and they can only run one way or the other. There is usually a noticeable resemblance between a circuit diagram and a stripboard layout for that circuit, but it is less striking than in the case of plain matrix layout.

One simple way of designing a stripboard layout for small projects, such as the amplifier described above, is to number the various component junctions starting with one for the earth rail and gradually working upwards to the other supply rail which has the highest number. You can be fairly random about where you place the numbers which occur between the supply rails, and this is by no means critical. However, make sure that all the components which are to be mounted on the panel have a number associated with each leadout, and only one number.

The next step is to take a stripboard panel which has the same number of strips as there are numbers on the circuit diagram, plus say an extra three strips to provide a space for the mounting holes. The board should be fairly wide so that there is plenty of space for the components. Any excess board can be carefully cut off later. If the lowest strip is numbered 1, the one above it 2, and so on, you will then have a corresponding number on the board for each one on the circuit diagram. Each component junction on the circuit is represented by a copper strip on the board.

Wiring the components onto the panel is then very simple. If, for example, the leadouts of a transistor connect to points 1 (emitter), 2 (base), and 3 (collector) on the circuit diagram, then on the stripboard its emitter is soldered to strip 1, the base to strip 2, and the collector to strip 3. If this is then carried out for all the other components, they must obviously be connected together in the correct manner.

By using this method the circuit diagram of Figure 31 could be transformed to the stripboard layout of Figure 32. This diagram shows the way in which stripboard panels are usually illustrated in magazines and books, with both sides of the panel being shown. Really this is self explanatory.

There are limitations to this method of producing a stripboard layout, the primary one being that it cannot be easily used for large circuits. There would then be so many wiring junctions that an impractically large number of copper strips would be

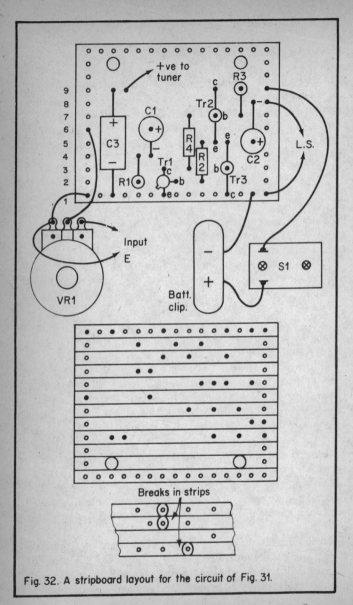

Fig. 32. A stripboard layout for the circuit of Fig. 31.

70

needed. For larger projects it is normally necessary to cut some of the copper strips so that they can be used to provide two or more wiring junctions, one each side of each cut.

A special tool known as a spot face cutter is available for making these breaks in the copper strips, but it can also be done using a sharp knife, or a small drill bit held in the hand. If the latter method is used, a drill bit of about 4 mm in diameter is suitable for 0.1 in. matrix board, and a drill of about 6 mm in diameter should be used for 0.15 in. matrix board. Like plain matrix board, stripboard is only available with these two pitches. Incidentally, the drill bit is hand held rather than mounted in a drill, since with this alternative method it is too easy to not only cut the copper, but also drill well into the board.

On component layout diagrams breaks in the copper strips are usually shown on the underside view of the panel in the manner shown in Figure 32. There are other ways, but they are all fairly obvious and require no amplification here.

Construction

The initial stages of construction for a stripboard project are much the same as for a plain matrix one. The board is cut to size, any rough edges are filed smooth, and the mounting holes are drilled. Then the procedure is slightly different, and the next step is to make any breaks in the copper strips that may be required. In this case of course, there are none, but more often than not it is necessary to make several breaks. It is advisable to make these breaks at an early stage, since they are easily forgotten if put off until later.

Then the actual wiring of the panel can commence, and the method of soldering components to a copper clad panel was described earlier. Sometimes it is necessary to use link wires, or bridges as they are occasionally called, to connect some of the copper strips together. It is a good idea to solder these in first as these are another example of something which is easily forgotten if left until later.

When completed, the panel can be connected to the rest of the circuit. All this wiring for the simple amplifier is illustrated in Figure 31.

As was the case with plain matrix board, pins can be used to make the connections between the panel and the leads which connect it to other parts of the circuit. This conveys the same advantages as for a plain matrix board. Single sided pins are usually used with stripboard, and these are inserted from the copper side of the panel and push as far in as they will go. They fit almost flush with the panel on the coppered side. They are then soldered in and used in the normal way.

If the amplifier is to be used in conjunction with the radio tuner which was described earlier, instead of the output of the tuner connecting to SK1, it instead connects to VR1 of the amplifier. Make sure that the connections are the right way round as they are not reversible. The battery clip and on/off switch are omitted from the tuner, which then obtains its positive supply rail connection from the amplifier (see Figure 31), instead of from S1. The negative supply rail connection is made via the leads which connect to the volume control.

It is as well to remember that the glue which bonds the copper strips to the sheet material does not have infinite strength. If, for instance, a component is mounted in the fashion shown in Figure 33, then any sideways pressure or pressure from above could rip the copper away from the backing material. This is known as 'de-laminating', and it frequently results in at least one break in the copper close to the point at which it occurs.

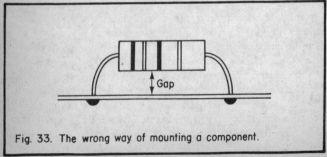

Fig. 33. The wrong way of mounting a component.

The most vulnerable points in this respect are at the edges of panels. Heat tends to weaken most adhesives, and so care must be exercised during and immediately after the soldering of a component.

It is not usual to expect the copper strips to provide the sole mechanical support for large or heavy components, and these should be firmly bolted to the panel as well.

Finally, it should perhaps be pointed out that although stripboard is probably the quickest and most convenient form of construction for most projects, it does have some limitations. The main one is that there is a small bit significant capacitance between adjacent copper strips, and this can cause problems if stripboard is employed in R.F. (radio frequency) circuits. It is not, therefore, often used in projects such as radio receivers, R.F. signal generators, and similar applications.

Even if used with certain audio frequency circuits this capacitance between strips can cause problems. This does not arise with the simple amplifier which was described earlier since it has only a modest voltage gain and a relatively narrow bandwidth. However, many modern items of audio equipment have both high gains and frequency responses which extend well into the radio frequency spectrum. This can lead to violent instability if a careless layout is used.

It is always the rule that the input circuitry of high gain amplifiers should be kept well away from the output circuitry whatever form of construction is used. When using stripboard you should bear in mind that although the input components may be mounted at one end of the board with the output ones at the other, this does not guarantee good isolation between the two, because the copper strips run the full length of the board. This should be kept in mind when designing ones own layouts.

Printed Circuit Boards
While this is admittedly the best form of construction in many ways, it is not really a good starting point for the beginner.

However, once you have gained a little experience with other constructional methods it is well worthwhile to try a project which uses an etched circuit board. Such projects almost invariably achieve a much more professional internal finish than those which use other forms of circuit board.

A printed circuit board (p.c.b.), or etched circuit board as it is sometimes known, has similarities to both plain matrix and stripboards. If you imagine a plain matrix board, except with copper strips rather than the component leadout wires being used to facilitate the wiring, then basically you have in mind a printed circuit board. It is different to stripboard in that the copper backing is not limited to rows of parallel strips, and the copper backing can be any desired pattern. Of course p.c.b.s have to be custom built to suit a particular circuit and component layout, and so they do not have a matrix of holes. These are only drilled where components are actually going to be mounted.

There are a few firms who will supply p.c.b.s for some of the more popular projects which are featured in the various electronic magazines, and so it is sometimes possible to use a p.c.b. even if you do not wish to etch your own. In fact, some of these firms will produce any p.c.b. design to special order, but the cost in one off quantities is too high to be a practical proposition for most constructors.

If you wish to use p.c.b.s more than occasionally, there is therefore little choice but to etch them yourself. It must be pointed out right from the start that etching p.c.b.s involves the use of a corrosive chemical which can be harmful to health if it is ingested, or even if it is splashed onto the skin or into the eyes. The chemical is ferric chloride, which although one of the least hazardous of possible etchants, is still poisonous and can harm skin. If any comes into contact with the skin it must therefore be washed off immediately. When etching p.c.b.s, do not use containers which are also used in the preparation of food.

Ferric chloride tends to stain yellow just about anything it comes into contact with, and it is corrosive to many metals and other substances. Thus it is a good idea to immediately wash any object which happens to come into contact with this chemical.

Continuity Tester

As a practical example of a project constructed on a printed circuit board, the continuity tester circuit of Figure 34 will be used. A continuity tester is a very simple but, nevertheless, useful piece of test equipment. It is a device which gives some form of indication when a low resistance is present between two test prods. The indication can be either visual or aural, but it is usually an aural one since this does not require the user to look away from the test prods to see if there is electrical continuity between the two prods.

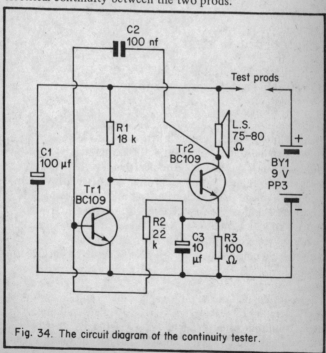

Fig. 34. The circuit diagram of the continuity tester.

COMPONENTS – CONTINUITY TESTER

Resistors

All are miniature $\frac{1}{8}$, $\frac{1}{3}$, $\frac{1}{4}$ or $\frac{1}{2}$ watt 5% types.

R1   18k (brown, grey, orange, gold)
R2   22k (red, red, orange, gold)
R3   100 ohms (brown, black, brown, gold)

Capacitors

C1   100mfd. 10 v.w. electrolytic.
C2   100nf type C280 (brown, black, yellow, black, red)
C3   10mfd. 10 v.w. electrolytic

Semiconductors

Tr1   BC109
Tr2   BC109

Miscellaneous

Materials for p.c.b.
Test prods.
PP3 battery and connectors to suit
75 to 80 ohm impedance speaker
Wire, solder, etc.

The continuity tester described here is of this type, and it produces an audio tone of about 400 Hz when the two test prods are shorted together. The beginner should find this device especially useful, since confusion can often arise when the inexperienced constructor has to deal with switches. It can often be impossible to ascertain which tag on the switch connects to which other tags in which switch position, unless one has previous experience with the particular type of switch involved, or a continuity tester is available so that a check can be made.

The circuit diagram of the unit is very simple, and the unit merely consists of a two stage direct coupled common emitter amplifier using Tr1 and Tr2. Tr1 has R1 as its collector load, and it is biased by R2. Tr2 has the loudspeaker as its collector load, and R3 is the emitter bias resistor. C3 is its bypass capacitor.

Positive feedback is applied to the amplifier via C2, and this causes the circuit to oscillate. The resultant output signal appears across the speaker and produces an audio tone.

C1 is an ordinary supply decoupling component, and this helps to keep the unit working efficiently when the battery is nearing exhaustion. No on/off switch is required, since no supply current can flow until a closed circuit is placed across the test prods.

Preparation

If you are designing your own printed circuit layout, this can be done in much the same way as for a plain matrix board, using very much the same layout that is used for the circuit diagram. If you draw onto a piece of paper a grid of lines so that rows of 5 mm square are produced, you can then draw the component layout onto this in exactly the same way as if it were a plain matrix board (the points at which the lines cross represents the holes in the board).

Apart from normal layout considerations, you must remember that it is not possible for the copper backing of a p.c.b. to cross over itself in the same way that the wires of a circuit diagram do. The wires of C2 and R2 of Figure 34 are good examples of this. It may sometimes be necessary to use link wires on the top side of the panel in order to overcome this, but with a little common sense it is usually possible to design the layout so that link wires are unnecessary. For instance, on the p.c.b. C2 could be mounted near to Tr2 collector with the lead which connects it to Tr1 base passing under the body of R1 (where there is obviously no other conductor).

When you have drawn the component layout onto the top side of the paper, and marked on the copper strips which join up the leadouts, the paper should be turned over and the copper pattern traced through onto the rear side of the paper Even if a fairly thick piece of paper is used, you will be able to trace this pattern through the paper if it is held up against a window so that the light comes through the paper.

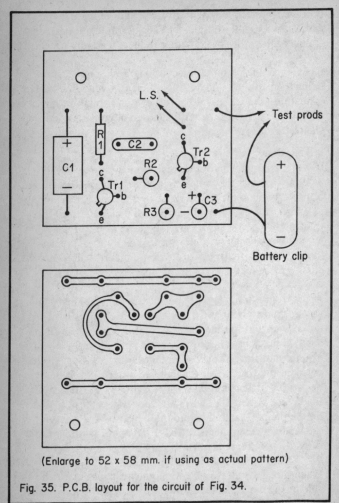

(Enlarge to 52 x 58 mm. if using as actual pattern)

Fig. 35. P.C.B. layout for the circuit of Fig. 34.

You then have a full size diagram of both the component layout (the top side of the paper) and the copper pattern (the underside of the paper). This should look something like the diagram of Figure 35 which is the suggested p.c.b. layout for the continuity tester.

This is not reproduced to actual size and should be scaled up to 52 x 58 mm before using as a pattern, by means of squared paper or a "Pantograph". In some books and magazines p.c.b. designs are reproduced to actual size, however you should always check this point before commencing construction. Whether you are working from your own drawing, or one in a book or magazine, the procedure for producing the p.c.b. is then the same.

The first item you need when making a p.c.b. is a piece of copper clad board. This is a sheet of insulation material which is completely covered with copper on one side. There is actually a type of board which is covered on both sides, but this is only used extremely rarely in amateur projects, and will not be considered here. Having obtained the board, the first job is to cut out a piece of the correct size using a hacksaw. For the continuity tester the board measures 52 x 58 mm.

It should perhaps be mentioned in passing that there are two types of copper clad board available, one has S.R.B.P. as the insulating material, and the other has glass fibre. The S.R.B.P. type is cheaper and is easier to cut, and it is perfectly satisfactory for the majority of projects. Glass fibre copper clad board is stronger, which can be an advantage where the board is being used to support some heavy component such as a mains transformer.

The next step is to thoroughly clean the copper surface of the board. You may think that this is unnecessary and that the copper looks reasonably bright and clean, but it is not advisable to omit this step. If you clean the board using a scouring pad or powder you will almost certainly find that it is noticeably cleaner afterwards. It is important that the copper is clean as the etchant will otherwise take a very long time to remove the unwanted copper and it could even fail to etch it at all.

Tracing
The copper pattern is then traced onto the copper side of the board. Be careful not to keep touching the copper side of the board once it has been cleaned, because this would result in greasy fingermarks being left on the board, and this could hinder the etching process.

The areas of copper which are to be left are then covered with an etch resist. There are many types of resist, but the one most commonly used is some form of quick drying paint. Nail varnish and car touch-up paint are often used. This is not because they are superefficient resists, but is simply because they dry very quickly, and so little time is wasted in this respect. Any oil based paint should prove to be an effective resist, provided an adequate amount is used.

In general, p.c.b.s tend to have copper patterns which are full of fine detail these days, and so it is essential to use a very fine brush to apply the resist. Do make quite sure that the areas of copper which are to be protected are adequately covered.

Fibre tipped etch resist pens are readily available these days, and they are increasingly popular. This is the type of resist the author always employs at present. These pens are charged with quick drying paint instead of ordinary ink, and so they can be used to fill in the pattern with a minimum of trouble. They are very much easier to use than the paint and brush method where very fine and intricate patterns are involved. Also, this is almost certainly the quickest method of applying the resist.

Some constructors prefer to use a self adhesive material such as Fablon as the resist. One way of using this is to cut thin strips of it, and then fix these to the board so that they cover up the appropriate areas of the copper. With any fairly intricate pattern this method is not really suitable.

An alternative method is to completely cover the copper side of the board with the material, and then trace the pattern onto this. A sharp modelling knife is then used to cut along the lines of the pattern and the unwanted material can then be peeled off. A very neat finish can be produced in this way, but it is a little more difficult than it sounds, and has a tendency to be very time consuming.

Etchant

It may be possible to obtain a solution of ferric chloride from a local chemist, but it is more likely that this will have to be mixed by the constructor. It is best to make the solution using ferric chloride crystals which may be available locally, or failing that there are at least two electronics mail order firms who will supply them. To look at, these look more like large rectangular lumps than crystals.

You will probably have to buy 500 gms of the chemical, which is enough to make about one litre of solution. The ferric chloride will not dissolve very quickly, and this process can be speeded up a little if the water is warmed before the crystals are added to it. Gentle stirring will also help here.

The ferric chloride may seem to be a little expensive, but one litre is enough to etch quite a large number of p.c.b.s. and so it should last quite a long while. The solution will be a dark yellow colour when it is first made up, but as it is used it will start to go green, and eventually blue. As it changes colour, the etching process will be found to take increasingly longer, and eventually the solution will be exhausted and will have to be replaced. Using fresh solution the etching time should be only about 20 minutes or so.

Another type of ferric chloride is available, and this is anhydrous ferric chloride. Unlike crystaline ferric chloride, this has no significant water content, and as a result it tends to react rather violently when added to water. A considerable amount of heat can be generated. It is much harder to make a solution using this material, but if you do decide to try it, you should note the following points.

Always add the chemical to the water, and not the other way round. Plastic dishes can melt with the heat that is produced, and so a glass one should be used (never put ferric chloride of any type into a metal container, as it will probably attack it). If the solution gets very hot, allow it to cool off before adding further ferric chloride.

You will probably need to experiment a little in order to find how much chemical is best for a given volume of water.

Etching

To etch the board it is placed in a flat bottomed glass or plastic dish and some etchant is poured onto it. Use plenty of etching fluid so that the board is well covered. The board should be placed copper side up so that you can see when the copper has been etched away. This process can be speeded up by warming the etching fluid. Gently rocking the dish occasionally will also help here, and this is virtually essential when the solution is nearing the end of its lifespan.

The etching process is one of replacement, with the copper from the board replacing the iron in the ferric chloride solution. Thus, with use, the yellow ferric chloride turns to blue copper chloride. The iron is deposited onto the surface of the board, and agitation of the dish helps to remove it, and so allow the reaction to take place unhindered.

When the etching has been completed, the board is removed from the dish and thoroughly rinsed under a tap. If a self adhesive plastic resist was used, this is then peeled off and the board is then cleaned using a scouring pad or powder. If a paint resist was used, then a scouring pad or powder can be used to both remove the resist and clean the board at the same time.

Drilling

In order to complete the p.c.b. it is then only necessary to drill the mounting holes for the components. A drill bit of no more than 1/16 in. or 1.6 mm should be used to do this, and really a 3/64 in. or 1.2 mm is better. Naturally, when using such fine drills it is necessary to take reasonable care when drilling the board since they are easily broken. Always drill from the copper side of the board since there is a likelihood of the copper backing being raised if you drill from the other side.

You may find that it is not possible to fit such small drill bits into your drill if it is a full size one. This can usually be overcome by tightly winding very thin cotton or wire around the shank of the drill bit in order to increase its effective diameter.

A miniature electric drill with a matching stand is a worthwhile investment if you are planning to frequently use home made p.c.b.s.

Finally, a list of the tools and materials required for home p.c.b. production is given below, and this should be useful to anyone commencing on this aspect of the hobby.

Copper laminate board.
Ferric chloride solution.
Scouring pad or powder and cloth.
Etch resist pen, or paint and fine brush, etc.
Flat bottomed plastic or glass dish of adequate dimensions to take p.c.b.s.
Miniature drill bit (about 1.2 to 1.6 mm in diameter).
(It is assumed that a hacksaw and drill are already to hand.)

Other Types
There are a few other types of circuit board which differ from the three types described above in some minor way, but at the time of writing these do not seem to be used very frequently, and so they will not be considered here. The way in which they are used should be fairly obvious to anyone who has read this chapter anyway.

Tagstrips

Tagstrips used to be a popular form of construction in the days when valves and point to point construction were popular, but they are not often used these days. They are sometimes employed in radio frequency circuitry, and in V.H.F. projects. They can also be useful in power supply circuits where large components are often involved. There are two basic types, and these are both illustrated in Figure 36.

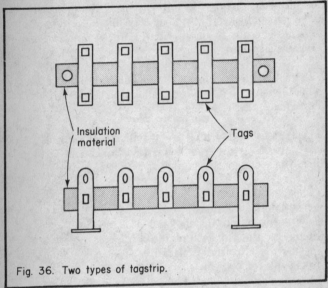

Fig. 36. Two types of tagstrip.

The components are simply wired to the tags in such a manner that the required circuit is formed, and the radio tuner circuit of Figure 25 for instance, could be wired up on a tagstrip in the manner shown in Figure 37.

There is a similar type of component known as a tagboard or a groupboard, and this is illustrated in Figure 37A. It is used in a similar way to a tagstrip, but tagboards are rarely used in modern home constructor designs.

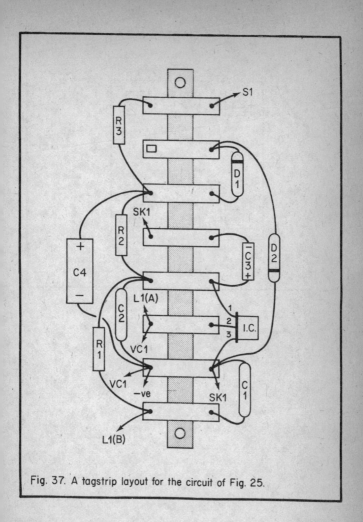

Fig. 37. A tagstrip layout for the circuit of Fig. 25.

85

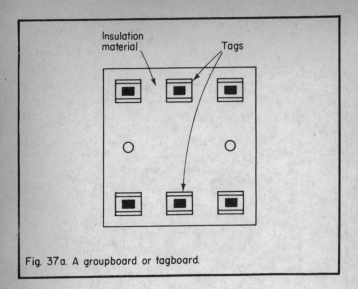

Fig. 37a. A groupboard or tagboard.

Chapter 4

CASES

So far in this book, only electrical construction has been dealt with. This is, of course, the majority of the constructional work as far as most projects are concerned. However, preparing cases and jobs of a similar nature account for a significant amount of the time taken in producing all but the most basic of devices.

Although the standard of exterior finish has no bearing on how well or otherwise a project works, you will almost certainly find that it is by this that most people judge your construction efforts. Also there is little point in constructing equipment with high standards of electrical workmanship and then spoiling the project as a whole by using a poorly constructed case with a scrappy front panel layout. It is true that a poor exterior finish will not degrade the performance of a piece of equipment, but it is worthwhile taking as much trouble on the casing as you do on the electronics. With the materials that are available today it is not too difficult to make projects that look very professional.

If you are not highly skilled at carpentry and metalwork this need not be a serious disadvantage these days. There is a very wide range of ready made cases available, and it is possible to construct simple but attractive cases which require a minimum of skill on the part of the builder.

Details of simple cases and obtaining a good exterior finish will be the main subject of this chapter.

Radio Case
In the previous chapter, details of a simple radio tuner and a matching amplifier were given. Now details of a suitable casing for these two items (plus the speaker and battery) will be provided so that a completely self contained M.W. receiver for loudspeaker reception can be built.

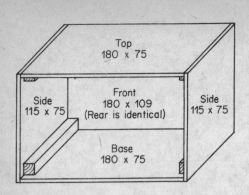

The corner pieces are each 69 x 10 x 10.
All dimensions are in m.m.

Fig. 38. Details of a simple case for the Tuner/Amplifier
combination.

Basic details of the case are provided in Figure 38. The front,
rear, base, top, and sides of the case are all made from either
faced hardboard or 3 mm plywood. Dimensions for each piece
are given in the diagram. It should be noted that a metal case
is not suitable for a radio which uses a ferrite aerial. The metal
would screen the aerial and thus prevent any significant signal
pick-up.

Both hardboard and plywood are easily cut using a tenon saw,
and so there should be no problems when cutting out the
required pieces. Hardboard does have a tendency to fray at
the edges when it is cut, but it is easily filed to a neat finish.

The pieces or the case, with the exception of the rear panel,
are glued together using simple butt joints. Four timber
corner pieces are used to give strength to the assembly. For
this type of job it is advisable to use a high quality gap filling
adhesive such as a quick setting epoxy type. Panel pins can

sometimes be helpful if they are used to hold the parts together while the adhesive sets, but often they are not required.

If any protruding edges are apparent when the case has been glued together, they should be filed down. Similarly, any gaps should be filled with plastic wood or a similar material. Then the case can be wiped with a damp cloth in order to remove any dust, and when it is absolutely dry, a self adhesive plastic material such as Fablon can be used to cover the case. Various colours and patterns are available, and a type which has a woodgrain pattern will provide an attractive finish to equipment which is intended for domestic use.

The rear panel of the case has a small hole drilled at each of its corners so that it can be fixed to corner pieces of the main casing by means of four small woodscrews. Of course, the rear panel is also covered with self adhesive plastic.

When using a material such as Fablon you should always try to cover the case using a single piece (or two pieces for a two part case such as that described here), since joins tend to pull apart with time due to the fact that the material shrinks very slightly. If it is necessary to have joins, arrange things so that they coincide with corners of the case, and preferably with lower corners where the joins are less likely to be seen.

Usually it is possible to use a single piece of material, and you should start with a piece of the plastic which has adequate dimensions. All the backing paper is removed from it, and then it is placed adhesive side up on a table. The case is then placed front downwards in the centre of the material, and a sharp modelling knife is used to cut through the plastic from each corner of the case to the adjacent corner of the plastic (Figure 39). You will then find that it is an easy matter to cover each side of the case, in turn, with the excess plastic being trimmed off using the knife. Some of the material should be wrapped over the edges of the case and into its interior.

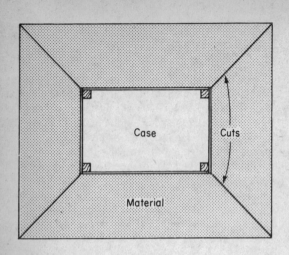

Fig. 39. Initial stages of covering a case with self adhesive plastic material.

If there are any holes of cutouts in the case, which there usually will be, simply ignore these when covering the case. The excess plastic which covers them can be cut off after the case has been fully covered. Try to avoid letting two sticky surfaces of the material come into contact with one another, as it can be very difficult to pull them apart without seriously stretching the plastic or even tearing it.

Drilling and Cutting

Wherever possible, it is advisable to make any necessary holes or cutouts in the case before the parts are assembled. This is not always possible, particularly when a complicated project is being constructed, or a ready made case is used. In this case only the front panel requires any drilling and cutting, and details of this are shown in Figure 40. It should perhaps be explained that it has been assumed here that a combined switch and potentiometer are used in the S1 and VR1 positions. The use of a combined volume and on/off switch is standard practice these days on this type of equipment.

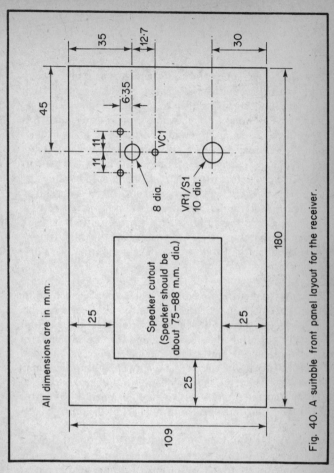

All dimensions are in m.m.

35
12·7
30
6·35
45
11
11
VC1
8 dia.
VR1/S1
10 dia.
180
Speaker cutout
(Speaker should be
about 75–88 m.m. dia.)
25
25
25
109

Fig. 40. A suitable front panel layout for the receiver.

I suppose that for the beginner the task of making the cutout for the speaker may be a little difficult. The easiest way of making this is using a fretsaw, or a coping saw should do just as well. It is very difficult to cut exactly along the line all the way around the cutout, and it is probably better to cut just inside the line and then file out the cutout to exactly the required size.

If neither a fretsaw nor a coping saw are available, then an alternative but slower method is to use a miniature round file.

VC1, if the specified or physically similar type is used, has a rather unusual mounting arrangement. It has a central 8 mm diameter mounting hole drilled to take its spindle, and three 4 mm diameter holes through which short countersunk 4BA screws pass. These are screwed into threaded holes in the front of the tuning capacitor. It is absolutely essential that these screws do not significantly penetrate beyond the inner edge of the capacitors front plate. If this should be allowed to happen it is possible that the component will be damaged, and it is virtually certain that the spindle will not rotate freely. If necessary, and in the author's experience, it always is, use washers or some other form of spacer over the mounting screws, between the front of the case and the front plate of the capacitor.

A piece of speaker fret or material is glued in place behind the speaker cutout. Any good general purpose adhesive can be used here. The speaker is glued in position behind the cutout, and a very powerful adhesive is required for this. An epoxy type is probably the most suitable. Only apply a very modest amount of glue to the speaker, and only apply it to the rim of the speaker. The reproduction quality of the speaker could be seriously impared if any adhesive should happen to get onto the diaphragm or some other moving part of the unit.

The two circuit boards are mounted at the bottom of the case with tuner board at the extreme right-hand side and the audio board immediately to the left of this. They are held in place using M3 or 6BA countersunk screws with nuts. It is advisable to use a few washers over the mounting screws, between the boards and the base panel of the case. Otherwise you will probably find that as the mounting nuts are tightened the boards will distort slightly, and they could even fracture. This is because the board is held flat against the case at the points where the mounting bolts and nuts are, whereas other areas are held slightly clear of the case by the soldered joints on the undersides of the panels.

It is sometimes said that spacers should be used to hold component panels well clear of wooden cases because wood is a poor insulator, and could therefore place a significantly low resistance between any copper strips which come into contact with it. In practice though, the resistance through wood seems to be far too high to cause any problems, provided the wood is not wet or even just slightly damp.

Mounting ferrite aerials is often something of a problem. Often they are mounted on a component panel, along with most of the other components, and so the aerial is mounted at the same time as the panel. Here a separate mounting is needed for the aerial, and probably the most simple method is to use a small block of wood. This should measure about 25 x 25 mm and have a 10 mm hole drilled through the centre. The aerial can then be threaded into the hole and glued in place using an epoxy adhesive (or any other high quality gap filling type). Then the block of wood is glued in place on the top panel of the case, and the aerial is thus mounted firmly in place.

There is a space for the battery at the bottom of the case on the extreme left-hand side. It is not a good idea to simply leave the battery loose inside the case, as this could easily lead to it damaging other components, in particular the ferrite rod aerial is vulnerable in this instance.

Various methods of mounting batteries are in common use at present. The simplest one is simply to stick the battery to the case using something like double-sided tape or Bostik Blue-Tack. A fairly large battery is used in this case, and so this method is not really suitable.

Here it will be necessary to construct a simple battery box, or battery compartment as it is sometimes called. This can be built

into the case in the manner shown in Figure 41. The rear
panel of the case forms the sixth side of the box so that there
is ready access to the battery (for replacement purposes)
when the rear of the case is removed, but the battery is held
in place when the rear panel is replaced.

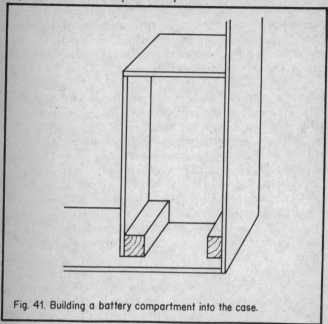

Fig. 41. Building a battery compartment into the case.

Unless the battery compartment is made very accurately it is
likely that the battery will still rattle around slightly. This can
be cured by using strips of self adhesive foam material on the
interior of the box. This foam material is sold in D.I.Y. shops
as draught excluder, and it often proves to be useful when
constructing electronic projects.

Legends
You may wish to apply legends to the front panel of the
receiver, or any other piece of equipment, and this certainly
helps to give finished projects a very neat and professional
look.

Two basic types of transfer are available, and probably the easiest type to use are the type which are printed on a self adhesive transparent plastic material. These have words which are commonly used on electronic projects (ON, OFF, VOLUME, etc.) as well as individual letters, numbers, electrical symbols, and even large, medium and small sizes dials.

In order to use these it is merely necessary to cut out the required word (or whatever), carefully peel off the backing paper, position the transfer over the appropriate position on the panel, and then press it firmly into place. Make quite sure that the panel is free from grease, moisture, and dirt before trying to apply this, or any other type of transfer.

The only real problem with this type of transfer is that it can be a little difficult to get them straight, and when you first use them you will probably find that the words are nearly all at slight angles to one another instead of all being horizontal. With a little practice however, this becomes far less of a problem, and it becomes possible to produce neatly lettered panels quickly and easily.

The other type of transfer which is in common use is the rub on type, such as Letraset, and most readers will be familiar with this type. The rub on transfers which are available to the amateur all seem to consist of individual letters and symbols, and this tends to make them rather difficult to use, especially in inexperienced hands.

Most sheets of rub-on lettering have a guide line which runs below each row of letters. The idea of this is that by drawing a guide line on the panel of the equipment, just below the area where the word is to be placed, by placing the guide line on the panel, a neat row of lettering must be produced. Of course, this only ensures that the letters are properly aligned vertically, and care must be taken to ensure that reasonably uniform spacing between letters is obtained.

It is usually possible to apply a suitable guide line to the panel of the equipment using a soft lead pencil. The line is easily rubbed off once it has served its purpose. This method is not really suitable when a plastic veneered front panel is used, and there are other panel finishes where it is not appropriate. In these instances a small strip of Sellotape can be used, with its upper edge forming the guide line.

When rubbing over the lettering do not use an implement which has a sharp point, as this usually results in a poor finish with small parts of each letter being absent. It is better to use a rather blunt pencil, and only apply light pressure. If after applying a letter to the panel you feel that it is unsatisfactory in some way, then it can usually be carefully rubbed off using a small piece of cloth.

Some rub-on transfers are supplied with a siliconised protective sheet which can be used to burnish finished words. In order to do this you simply place the siliconised sheet over the lettering and press it down very firmly using something like the rounded end of a screwdriver handle.

Not all rub-on transfers are supplied with a siliconised sheet, and these should be protected in some other way. This is not absolutely essential, and if the lettering is left to thoroughly harden, it will have a fairly tough finish. However, greater permanence will be provided if the panel is sprayed with a suitable lacquer.

If the panel already has a veneer of some kind, then spraying it with lacquer is probably not appropriate. Incidentally, a suitable aerosol clear lacquer spray should be available from the transfer supplier, and it is not a good idea to use a brush applied lacquer. The brushing process can damage the lettering. In fact some lacquers will simply dissolve the lettering, and can even attack plastic cases or veneers!

A simple way of protecting the panel legends is simply to cover them with small pieces of Sellotape, with due care being taken to ensure that no creases are produced in the tape. If this should happen, and you try to remove the tape so that it can be replaced, it is virtually certain that the lettering will adhere to the adhesive on the tape and will thus be removed from the panel as well.

Metal Case

Metal cases are popular in certain fields of electronics, such as test equipment, small audio gear, and Short Wave equipment. In some applications it is essential to use a metal case in order to provide screening for the circuitry. In other applications, such as Short Wave gear, it is convenient from the constructional point of view, and in others it is simply a matter of convention.

It is possible to obtain an extremely attractive finish from a metal housing, especially if it is painted using a two colour scheme. A wide variety of types and sizes of metal cases are available, and they are usually constructed from either steel or aluminium. Aluminium is preferred by most constructors since it is far softer than steel and is therefore much more easily worked. Some cases are constructed using a steel outer casing, with the front and rear panels (and chassis if fitted) being constructed from aluminium. The steel outer casing provides a very strong basic structure, while the parts of the case which are likely to need cutting and drilling done to them are made of aluminium.

If you wish to make your own metal cases they will need to be of all aluminium construction unless you have access to sophisticated metal working equipment. Such cases can be very simple, and details of a simple example are shown in Figure 42. This has been designed to accommodate the continuity tester which was described in the previous chapter.

Aluminium sheet is available in various thicknesses from about 10 to 20 s.w.g. (approx. 3.25 to 0.9 mm). Where it is necessary to make folds in the aluminium, as it is in this case, it is advisable to use a fairly thin gauge, and the author usually employs either 20 s.w.g. (0.9 mm) or 18 s.w.g. (1.2 mm).

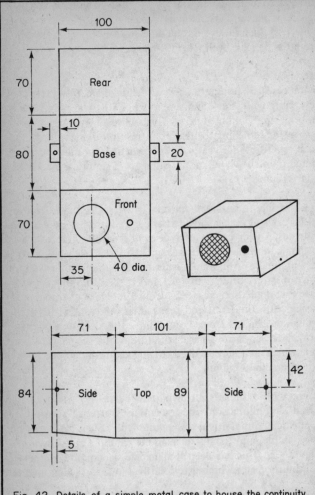

Fig. 42. Details of a simple metal case to house the continuity tester. It can be fitted with self adhesive cabinet feet.

Using the thicker gauge will produce a stronger case, but it will be harder to make the folds in the metal. Making a fold in aluminium that has a gauge of 16 or less is extremely difficult unless proper tools for the purpose are available.

The first process in the construction of the case illustrated in Figure 42 is to cut out two rectangles of aluminium, one measuring 220 × 120 mm, and the other measuring 243 × 89 mm. The former is for the base, front, and rear, and the latter will eventually form the top and side panels.

The normal way of cutting aluminium or other sheet metal, assuming a more sophisticated tool is not available, is to use a hacksaw. However, it is not easy to make a good job of long cuts using a hacksaw, and very long cuts are outside the range of a hacksaw. Guillotine tools intended for metal cutting are available from some D.I.Y. shops, and these usually produce quicker, neater results than can be attained using a hacksaw.

An alternative to these methods which the author has found to be extremely good is to use a sharp modelling knife. This is used to deeply score the aluminium along the required cut, and to do this it is necessary to repeatedly draw the blade across the metal. If the aluminium is then bent backwards and forwards along the score line several times, it will eventually fatigue and break. In order to obtain a straight score line it is necessary to use the edge of metal ruler or trysquare to guide the knife, and, of course, adequate care must be taken. Usually this method produces a very clean and straight edge when the cut has been made, and very little filing will be required.

When the two rectangles of metal have been cut out, then the excess pieces of aluminium are cut off so that the required shapes are produced. The hole in each side panel is then drilled, and these have a diameter of 4 mm.

A 40 mm diameter cutout in the front panel is required for the loudspeaker, and aluminium is soft enough for this to be made using a fretsaw or coping saw, even if metal cutting blades for these cannot be obtained. The author has always found ordinary wood cutting blades to be satisfactory, but these should preferably have fine teeth. A miniature round file can also be used, but will be much slower. A smaller hole is drilled to the right of the speaker cutout, and this is where the two test leads pass through the front panel. This hole must be fitted with a rubber or P.V.C. grommet eventually. The purpose of the grommet is to prevent the leads from rubbing against the metalwork, and eventually wearing through the insulation.

Folds

Provided a vice of adequate size is available, it is not too difficult to make good tight 90 degree folds in aluminium sheet. Wooden vices are less than ideal, but can usually be used satisfactorily. The important thing is to ensure that metal is gripped very tightly, as otherwise it will tend to shift in the jaws of the vice when you try to bend it.

When actually folding the aluminium it is important that fairly even pressure is applied over the entire length of the fold. Rather than try to fold the metal using ones hands directly onto the metal, it is better to use a strip of thick steel between ones hands and the metal. Interposing the strip of steel has two main effects, one of which is to maintain a fairly even pressure down the full length of the fold. The other is that it enables the pressure to be placed right down at the jaws of the vice, and this enables a very tight fold to be obtained.

It is essential that such a tight fold should be obtained as the case will otherwise look rather scrappy, and the two parts will not fit together very well. If a tight fold cannot be produced by hand it will be necessary to use a mallet to improve matters. Do not use a hammer as this will leave a series of dents in the metal, unless a block of wood is used between the aluminium and the hammer.

When all six folds have been made, the two sections of the case can be fitted together. The outer casing is used as a template with which the positions of the two holes in the brackets on the base panel are located. These holdes are drilled for 3.2 mm diameter. Two 6BA self tapping screws are used to hold the two parts of the case together.

Layout

The layout on the interior of the case is very simple, with the p.c.b. being mounted on the right-hand side of the case towards the rear, with the battery to the left of this The p.c.b. can be used as a sort of template with which the positions of its 3.2 mm mounting holes are found. Spacers about 6 mm long are used over the mounting bolts, between the p.c.b. and the case, in order to hold the connections on the underside of the board well clear of the metal base of the case. A spacer simply consist of a metal tube which has a hole through the centre which has a diameter to suit a particular screw size. There are more sophisticated ways of mounting a p.c.b. and holding it clear of a metal chassis or case, but they are not in common use by amateurs at the time of writing.

Speaker mounting and battery compartments were discussed earlier, and so they will not be covered in detail again here. The battery compartment used in the receiver described earlier was constructed from plywood or hardboard. The same method could be used here, but it would be more logical and neater to fabricate the battery box from a small piece of aluminium, and this is very easy to achieve.

Finishing

Commercially constructed metal cases usually seem to be finished with a plastic veneer, stove enamel paint, or are anodised. These all require techniques which are outside the scope of most amateurs, and so ordinary paint has to be used. Of course, a self adhesive plastic covering can be used, but this does not usually fit as well onto a metal case it does onto a wooden one. Also, a self adhesive plastic veneer can look rather out of place on a metal case unless you choose the colour and pattern very carefully.

Before painting a case you must ensure that it is free from dust, grease, and moisture. You must also use a primer, undercoat, and top coat that are suited to one another. Do not be tempted simply to apply the top coat direct onto the bare metal of the case. This will simply result in the slightest knock or scrape removing some of the paint and exposing bare metal. It is a good idea to rub the surface of the case with fine emery paper prior to applying the primer coat. This has the effect of covering the case with numerous fine scratches, and these provide a mechanical key for the paint to cling to.

Conventionally the outer casing of this type of cabinet is finished in a fairly dark coloured paint while the front, rear, and base are finished in a light colour. A very attractive finish can be obtained by using dark blue hammer finish paint for the outer casing and white enamel for the rest of the case. A good finish can be obtained from hammer finish paint if it is brushed on, but it is probably better if the enamel is sprayed on. Aerosol spray paints are readily available, and so no special spraying equipment is required.

Plastic Cases
It is possible for the home constructor to build his or her own plastic cases, but this is not really something that the author would recommend. Sheets of plastic are rather hard to obtain, and at present they are extremely expensive. Some extremely smart plastic or plastic and metal cases are available, and it is usually better to use one of these (or some other form of home made case) rather than construct ones own plastic cases.

The technique of home constructing a plastic case is much the same as for building a plywood or hardboard one. However, if an accurate job is made of it, there is no need to use a plastic veneer on the case.

Incidentally, it is very easy to accidentally scratch a plastic case when working on it, but provided the scratch is not very deep, it can be removed by rubbing over the damaged part of the case with a rag soaked in metal polish.

Finally

The projects which have been described in this book were chosen because they cover just about everything the beginner is likely to encounter in electronic construction, from common everyday jobs like soldering, to the more unusual ones like cutting a ferrite rod. However, it is not possible to cover absolutely everything you will need to know when constructing projects since many projects these days are of a very specialised nature, and employ constructional techniques which are unique. Fortunately, unusual constructional techniques are usually dealt with in great detail in the magazine or book concerned, and so there is no point in discussing any of them in great detail here anyway.

Of course, there are a few important points which have not been dealt with so far, and one example of this is the mounting of power devices. This includes such things as power transistors, high current diodes, high power triacs, etc. These semiconductor devices all generate a certain amount of heat during normal use, and are usually intended to operate at quite high temperatures (they are often too hot to touch even under correct operating conditions). It is usually necessary to mount power devices on a heatsink of some kind in order to dissipate the heat that is produced. Otherwise the components would simply increase in temperature until they exceeded their maximum operating temperature. This is highly undesirable since apart from destroying the device concerned, side effects can be produced. For instance, the breakdown of one device can lead to a short circuit which in turn leads to the destruction of other components. Overheated components can even explode or catch fire. It is therefore important to ensure that adequate heatsinking is provided for power devices.

Details of the required heatsink should be provided in the book or magazine, and it usually just consists of an area of aluminium sheet. Very often the metal case or chassis of the equipment is used as the heatsink.

Probably the most common types of power device are those which are contained in the diamond shaped TO3 style case, or one of the similar but slightly smaller cases. The case of these devices connects to one of the terminals of the component, and for instance, the case of a TO3 power transistor always connects to the collector. Very often the heatsink will be in electrical contact with some part of the circuit (usually one of the supply rails), and this makes it necessary to insulate the device from its heatsink. In order to do this an insulating kit consisting of a mica washer and two plastic bushes is required. The way in which they are used is illustrated in Figure 43(a). Incidentally, an easy way of locating the positions of the four mounting holes for the component is to use a mica insulating washer as a template.

When you have drilled the mounting holes, always remove any burrs using a large drill bit held in the hand, or a sharp modelling knife. Mica washers are very thin, and must be so as they would otherwise severely hinder the flow of heat from the device into the heatsink. Any burrs would almost certainly cut straight through the washer. Mica washers are easily damaged, and should be handled carefully.

The method of insulating a TO126 device (or similar single screw fixing devices) is shown in Figure 43(b). Figure 43(c) shows the method of mounting and insulating stud type devices.

When a power semiconductor is being used near the limit of its power handling capability it is often necessary to use a smear of silicon grease (or silicon grease substitute) between the body of the device and the heatsink, or between the device and the mica washer. This ensures that a good thermal contact is provided between the components and the heatsink.

When you have finished mounting a power semiconductor which is supposedly insulated from its heatsink, it is a good idea to check using a continuity tester that it is actually insulated from the heatsink. A damaged mica washer or

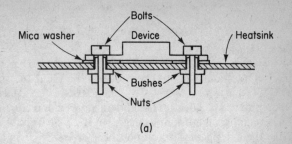

(a)

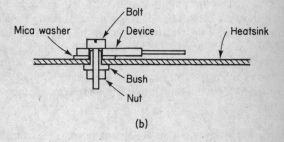

(b)

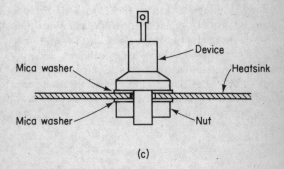

(c)

Fig. 43. Methods of insulating power devices from their
heatsink: (a) TO3 (or similar), (b) TO126 (or similar),
(c) stud mounting device.

something of this nature can lead to disastrous consequences if you switch on the equipment without having taken any corrective measures.

Delicate Devices

There are some devices which are rather delicate, and can be damaged by static charges. These are MOSFET and dual gate MOSFET transistors, MOS I.C.s, and CMOS I.C.s. Most contemporary MOS devices have internal protection circuitry which minimises the risk of damage, but it is still advisable to handle these devices as little as possible.

MOS transistors are sometimes supplied with a metal clip which short circuits all the leads together. This clip should not be removed until the electrical work on the project has been completed. MOS and CMOS I.C.s are usually supplied with their leads embedded in a conductive foam material, or they have some other form of protective packaging. Do not remove them from this packaging until it is time to connect them into circuit.

You should always use a soldering iron having an earthed bit (most types do) when soldering any MOS device. It is a good idea to use an integrated circuit socket for CMOS and MOS I.C.s, since it is then unnecessary to do any soldering while the devices are in circuit. It is a good idea to use a socket on any fairly expensive I.C. anyway, as soldering I.C.s usually invalidates the manufacturers guarantee. It also eliminates any risk of damaging the I.C. through overheating when it is soldered in, although I.C.s are fairly tough devices, and there is not a great risk of this happening.

COMPONENT REFERENCES

Listed below are the abbreviations for component names which are used on circuit diagrams, components lists, etc.

A or Ae	Aerial
B or BY	Battery
C	Capacitor
CH	Chassis
CSR	Silicon Controlled Rectifier (S.C.R. or Thyristor)
D	Diode
E	Earth
F or FS	Fuse
L	Inductor (coil)
M or ME	Meter
MIC	Microphone
PCC	Photocell
RL	Relay
S	Switch
SK	Socket
T	Transformer
Tr	Transistor (any type)
VC	Variable capacitor
VR	Variable resistor or potentiometer
WD	Warning device (bell or buzzer).

Notes

Notes

Please note overleaf is a list of other titles that are available in our range of Radio, Electronics and Computer Books.

These should be available from all good Booksellers, Radio Component Dealers and Mail Order Companies.

However, should you experience difficulty in obtaining any title in your area, then please write directly to the publisher enclosing payment to cover the cost of the book plus adequate postage.

If you would like a complete catalogue of our entire range of Radio, Electronics and Computer Books then please send a Stamped Addressed Envelope to:

BERNARD BABANI (publishing) LTD
THE GRAMPIANS
SHEPHERDS BUSH ROAD
LONDON W6 7NF
ENGLAND